CARLOS CUAUHT

FLYING OVER QUICKSAND

A NOVEL ON PERSONAL VALUES TO OVERCOME ADVERSITY AND SUCCEED

Ediciones Selectas Diamante, S.A. de C.V.
Books that transform lives

FLYING OVER QUICKSAND

Original Title: Volar sobre el pantano
This book was translated by: Marianne Walker de Navarro, M.A.
Cover: *"La Madelaine, risen to the sky"*
Giovanni Lanfranco (1582-1647)

Books that transform lives
Convento de San Bernardo No. 7
Jardines de Santa Monica, Tlalnepantla
Estado de Mexico, C.P. 54050, Ciudad de Mexico.
Tels. and Fax: 525-397-79-67, 525-397-31-32
E-mail:ediamante@prodigy.net.mx
Member of the Mexican Chamber of the Editorial Industry

ISBN: 968-7277-45-9

PRINTED IN MEXICO

FLYING OVER QUICKSAND

CONTENTS

Zahid:

From the first time I saw you

I realized you were born to be successful.

This book is for you.

1

Loneliness

Lisbeth seemed confused by my insistence.

She put her glass on the table and looked at me in a straightforward way for a few seconds.

"I don't understand you," she said to me, "we had agreed to forget that matter and now you want to relive it."

The breeze from the sea rustled her long hair. I watched it, as I trembled, holding my sister's letter in my hand.

"From what I know, Alma did not suffer like you did," I said to her, "it certainly isn't necessary to live through something so terrible to fall apart."

"Fall apart? Why do you think that she has fallen apart?"

"I don't know. Perhaps I am misinterpreting things or getting her letter mixed up with my nightm..."

I stopped. Lisbeth watched me silently. I shrugged and continued:

"The nightmares have come back."

She nodded slowly.

"I know."

I walked up to her.

"They're so real *again*... I didn't want to worry you."

"But, the physician told us that the dreams would not repeat themselves unless..."

She hesitated.

"Say it."

"Unless you experienced a similar anguish again."

"Exactly. That's why I need *you* to tell me the story that I never wanted to hear before... I need you to tell me what a woman feels when she's been a victim of abuse. In all my nightmares, I hear my sister Alma repeatedly screaming, crying and begging me for help. I wake up sweating, haunted as if she were there, with her lonely expression needing affection and understanding..."

A flock of pelicans flew over our heads.

Lisbeth knew that she had no other alternative, that I wouldn't give up. She sighed.

"All right, I'll tell you."

When my father burst into my bedroom, I was getting ready to go to sleep.

Strangely, he didn't knock at my door. He entered in a frenzy as if the house was on fire.

"You have to come with me! Get dressed, quickly."

It was an order.

"What happened?"

"Hurry up! Don't ask. Just come."

Only something very serious could make him act like that at ten o'clock at night.

"I'm waiting for you...!"

"I'm coming."

I put on whatever clothes I could find and left my bedroom, feeling scared. Without saying a word, Dad walked directly to the front door. I followed him. My mother was nervously standing there and when we walked by her, she avoided my eyes.

The car was running, the door was open and the lights were on. It was as if he had stopped the vehicle only to pick me up.

"Where are we going?"

He didn't answer. He was breathing hard, which made his face seemed deformed. With the same furious look on his face, driving wrecklessly, we headed downtown.

"How long have you dated that young man?" he asked.

"Where are we going, Dad?"

"I asked you something."
"Four months."
"Has he made you try any drugs?"
"Dad, what's wrong with you?"
Suddenly, he made a right turn and we penetrated into a dark dangerous slum. After several turns, driving with no caution, he stopped in front of six or seven teenagers who were sitting in a semicircle on the sidewalk, doing drugs. Alienated from reality and stoned out of their minds, they were clumsily sharing their dope.
"Do you see?" my father was out of control.
I shook my head.
"What is it that you want me to see?"
"Watch closely."
He bent down to reach for a flashlight under his seat and, while trying to light it, one of the intoxicated girls approached us. My father aimed the light at her. She was young, barely sixteen or seventeen years old, dirty, without a bra and her blouse open halfway down.
"Don't open the door," exclaimed Dad.
Tumbling towards the car, the girl put her mouth on my window and slid down slowly until her repugnant tongue ended up licking the glass.
"Let's go," I said, shivering by the sudden terror that the scene produced. "I don't know what you're trying to show me."
"Look."
The young girl disappeared under my door. Dad used the flashlight to light up the small group of human scum.
"Do you see him now?"
The light beam found the face of a young man that I knew very well.
"Martin...?"
"Yes."
"It can't be... He only resembles him..."
"It's him."
"But..."
A lacerating anguish began to asphyxiate me. I opened the door

and got out. Without meaning to, I stepped on the girl that was hallucinating almost under the car. She didn't complain. I walked with tremulous steps towards the druggies. My father went after me.

"It's dangerous..."

Martin raised his head and stared directly at me as if attempting to recognize who I was.

My tears of fear turned into tears of anger. I wanted to beat him, kill him, or kill myself... I cursed the hour in which he stopped to ask me out, the hour in which, without really knowing him, I accepted, the hour in which...

"Hi...," he mumbled, "I need... come... come closer... I need..."

"Let's go," insisted my father.

"Wait. He wants to tell me something."

"Let's go!"

He pulled me to the car and pushed the girl aside, then opened my door and drove away at full speed. For a good while on the way back to the house we didn't speak. I was staring into space, my eyes full of tears, feeling a lump of anger in my throat.

"I know how you feel, Lisbeth," he finally said, "but there are many men in the world. This fellow deceived you... And, I'm sorry to say this but, *it's good* that you saw him like this now, before he hurt you or got you into drugs too."

I didn't answer... How could I tell him I felt like I didn't receive enough love and attention at home? It wasn't important for me to live in an overprotected cotton-lining if no one was really interested in who I was or what I did, making life seem worthless to me. How could I tell him that precisely because I felt that I had an empty existence I had given myself to Martin... even without loving him or really knowing who he was...?

"I feel devastated too because of your disappointment," he said. "Last week you said that you really loved him."

The week before, I had wanted to speak but no one stopped what they were doing to truly listen to me, so I could only say that I was in love with Martin, our lifelong neighbor. But that was not what I had wanted to say... it wasn't only that...

He parked his car in front of my boyfriend's house, got out and knocked at the door. The father came out, they shook hands and a distressing conversation began between them. Dad explained what we had seen, making exaggerated facial expressions. His listener lost all color. The mother appeared on the scene; she reacted with obvious aggressiveness, yelling, insulting and blaming him. I bowed my head and closed my eyes.

How could I have gotten involved with him? He was always a distant neighbor. I never really liked him. When I was a little girl, I would watch him from my window while he killed birds with his slingshot and threw stones at buses. Almost four months ago, we ran into each other at a park near our neighborhood. I still didn't like him, but I felt very lonely and I accepted his invitation to go out... Since our first date I noticed something strange: his sudden mood swings, his sadism, his red eyes. He was sometimes violent and sometimes sweet. What could he have wanted to tell me a few minutes before?

Dad got back in the car and left the unfortunate couple arguing.

My house was only half of a block away so we quickly arrived home, but we could still hear the neighbors fighting.

Mom was waiting for us. As soon as we walked in, she wanted to comfort me, but I shrugged her off and went to my bedroom. I almost bumped into my two sisters who watched me as if I were a ghost.

In my bedroom, I paced back and forth, threw myself on the bed and cried for almost an hour.

Suddenly the phone rang.

"It's Martin's father," Mom said, "he wants to speak with you."

I froze, not knowing what to do.

"Please open the door."

"Leave me alone."

"We don't want you to be alone right now."

The word "alone" went straight to my brain like a dagger to the heart... How could she say that? How did she dare...?

Then, I opened the door and faced my family. My mother and sisters were in front, my father behind them.

"You shouldn't feel so bad... We know that you wanted to get married but, as you can see, he's no good for you..."

I interrupted my consolers abruptly. I never thought I would blurt it out to them like this, but if they wanted to understand the magnitude of my misery, they had to know all the facts.

"I'm pregnant with his baby."

As soon as I said that, there was a deadly silence.

"What did you say?"

"What you heard. That I'm pregnant... I wanted to tell you the other day..."

Their astonishment was unreal. They delayed in assimilating the shocking news, but as soon as the truth sunk in, their reaction was volatile.

"How could you? What were you thinking of? Are you stupid?"

I shrugged my shoulders. After giving them the news, my rage dissipated and I began to crumble, to understand precisely that: how stupid I had been.

"Do you love him?"

"Why did you go to bed with him?"

"Did he force you?"

I denied all the questions shaking my head. To speak about melancholia, confusion or low self-esteem, would have sounded trivial. I knew they wanted reasonable arguments, disputable reasons...

"Damn," my father said, pushing everyone aside and entering my room. He grabbed the reading lamp and broke it into pieces; he grunted while yelling *"why?"* again and again. He approached me with decisive strides as if prepared to slap me, but instead grabbed me by the shoulders and screamed at me:

"Have you tried drugs?"

"No, no."

He pushed me back and I fell.

When my face was just a few inches from the floor, the impact hit me and I understood that I had completely fallen... physically, intellectually, spiritually, morally, mentally, intimately, psychologically, emotionally...

"How far along are you?" my sister asked.

I answered by showing three fingers on my left hand...

"That's it, cry now!" my father yelled. "You don't have any other option. You've ruined your life and, furthermore, you've dishonored the family. Your little adventure affects us all... especially your sisters. You're the oldest one, don't you realize the example that you're giving the other two?" The words got stuck in his throat, he took a deep breath trying to control himself. "I can't believe you've done this! I always thought that you would be at the top. You have no idea how disappointed I am," he corrected himself, "that we all are of you..."

The worst part about that last phrase was that no one jumped up to defend me, neither my sisters nor my mother.

Lying on the floor, I wanted to lift my head and ask my Dad what happened to everything he had said to me in the car: *"I feel devastated too because of your disappointment."* I wanted to reproach my mother and question her why she had said: *"We don't want you to be alone at this time..."* Had they said it without meaning it? Or was it that they were at my side ready to console me only in the case that it was a simple personal disappointment, but of course not if my mistake affected their positive parental image; their status of *"nice"* people who do everything right as well as their damned family name, representative of virtuous morals that couldn't afford the luxury of having a single mother in their home?

Martin's father was waiting on the phone for me. I wanted to get up, but I couldn't. Mother sat on her haunches and put her hand on my back; I wanted to move it, to push her hand away, to tell her that I was disgusted by her selfish position, but I had lost all my energy. I felt small, lifeless... like the most despicable worm.

My sisters tried to move me. They couldn't. I felt I was a rejected piece of garbage, a fallen tree made into firewood, an entity without any self-love, who was crying her eyes out, believing I deserved the worst for not having thought things through. I felt I didn't deserve to be alive, hating the baby that I was carrying inside of me and at the same time loving him. He was my accomplice... my only defenseless friend that understood my pain and who, without being the one to blame, was guilty of all... because of his existence.

I felt like a mother for the first time. A mother that was all ALONE.

Making a superhuman effort I stood up and went to the phone to talk to Martin's father.

"Hello?"

"Lisbeth?"

"Yes."

"They found my son in very serious condition."

"Where?

He gave me the address of a hospital and when he was going to ask me something more, like a robot, without listening to anything else, I let the receiver drop on the table and headed out to the street. I didn't know that by leaving the house I was about to enter a terrible swamp filled with desperation and terror.

"Where are you going?"

I didn't answer.

Years later, I now realize that true *lonelines*s is what leads us, with its devilish melody, into the mire. *Loneliness* is the edge of the quicksand where the destruction begins for any human being... Once in it, we start to be pulled towards its thickest entrails... And one should understand this very well: **loneliness does not mean to be *physically* alone, it means a lack of affection...** One can create, meditate, plan and work, being completely physically isolated and still feel happy, provided in your soul you have the energy of knowing you are loved by someone... even though that someone is not there... On the other hand, another person can be surrounded by a lot of people and feel fatally unhappy knowing that he is ignored and no one cares. Loneliness leads to alcoholism, drugs, adultery, suicide... Without a doubt, that night I fell uncontrollably into quicksand.

2

The law of forewarnings

Lisbeth stopped telling her story.

The story not only hurt me, but it stirred up feelings of nervousness, jealousy and rage.

"I told you that it would be hard to talk about this."

"No. I mean, yes. The truth is, I'm shocked."

She slapped at a bug that stung her arm, but missed.

"Shall we go in the house?" she asked, as she stood up and walked to the door without waiting for an answer.

I followed her. In that huge garden, right next to the beach, we had found a paradise of peace to share our private thoughts and a perfect place for fun.

I closed the aluminum sliding door and moved close to her.

"Please continue."

"But, first tell me. What are you up to?"

"I only want to know how you solved your problem of an unwanted pregnancy."

"Why are we talking about this now? It's something that we agreed never to discuss again."

She was right and I couldn't conceal the truth from her for long.

"I just received a letter from my sister."

"Alma?"

I nodded...

"But, we just moved here. How did she find you?"

"She sent it to my office in Mexico City. From there, they forwarded it to me. This letter has made me think about things that I can't handle all by myself, that's why I asked you to talk about the past..."

"Zahid, your attitude is scaring me. What's going on? Does she have something to do with me?"

"In a way. For example, what you just told me, helps me to understand her better. *The lack of affection, the loneliness that kills, the quicksand that asphyxiates.* Alma was a witness to my family's worst tragedies but no one took her into account, no one asked for her opinion; if there was something serious that had to be discussed, she was told to leave, she was underestimated by all, treated as if she were a hindrance. Sometimes, you could see a great tenderness and an unbelievable need for love in her face... You know something? Having received this letter precisely at this moment, is the worst possible timing for me."

I sat down next to my wife and opened the envelope very slowly.

"I'm going to read the letter to you. Listen carefully and tell me if you can decipher anything between the lines that perhaps I, as a man, haven't grasped."

"Okay."

I unfolded the blue paper and my sister's message displayed itself before my eyes. Alma's handwriting had always been a fine and symmetrical calligraphy, however, the lines now seemed shaky and in some areas, excessively light.

I began to read without being able to avoid a gnawing feeling of despair.

Zahid:

We all have a different threshold of pain. Some people, with a simple stomach infection realize the fact that they should change their nutritional habits, that they should exercise and live a healthier lifestyle; a small stimulus is sufficient to lead them to reflect and to change... Others, in contrast, ignore the small warnings and need to be dying with acute cirrhosis or with chest angina to say to themselves: "Wow, now I do have to look after myself..." It's a matter of how you are.... of how you react...

I believe that you're one of those who react to the slightest stimulus; one of those who don't wait for greater warnings. I, on the other hand, am one of those who always believe that things will improve on their own... Now it's too late...

I stopped reading. My mind was blank. It was the third time that I had read these words and once again they confirmed that something bad had happened to Alma.

"Go on, Zahid, what else does she say?"

I need to see you. I can't think of anyone else. Knowing what you did for me has kept me alive the last months, but I confess to you that in periods of confusion my memory becomes grotesque and blurry... Knowing that you had the courage and the love to defend me and that you were willing to give half of your sight for me, has provided me with the energy to know that I was loved once. I know that every morning, when you look at yourself in the mirror, you remember me, and I, forgive me, feel a little better for that...

I stopped. Lisbeth didn't insist that I continue. Now she realized the seriousness of the matter... After a few seconds I began reading in a low voice.

Perhaps you can't help me. I know that you'd give your full sight for me, if it were necessary, but I don't want to be another burden. I hope that you come. Here the time goes by very slowly. We can talk like we did when we were together in your hospital room, where you were in bed after having lost your left eye. Except now I'm the one who is in bed and, just like you, I've lost something irreplaceable. And, you know what? The truth is I wish I wasn't a woman; I wish I wasn't so weak; I wish I hadn't buried myself in my own misery; I wish I had never been born...

Forgive me if I'm causing you any unnecessary worry, but sooner or later I had to speak. Your pain was known by all and that helped you heal; mine on the other hand, was secret and it has been killing me slowly throughout the years... As you can see, sometimes I still think with some lucidity, but only sometimes...

Zahid. If you can't come to see me, please, don't tell anyone where I am.

I love you,
Alma

There was a dense and frozen silence in the room.

"The envelope doesn't have a return address," I said, feeling confused, "On the back there are only three words: St. John's Hospital."

I fidgeted with the sheet without saying anything more. I had arrived at the conclusion that it could only be a hospital specializing in traumatology, since she said *having lost, like I did, something irreplaceable...* Or, perhaps... a psychiatric one...

"You lost your eye defending your sister?"

I stood up and walked around the living room. Certainly, the origin of my nightmares was precisely having kept many things to myself.

"At that time, Alma stayed with me day and night, next to my bed," I replied incoherently, trying to avoid her question. "She felt guilty... but also admiration and gratitude for my sacrifice. Her self-esteem was demolished..." A depressing heaviness invaded me as I added, "You have no idea how hurt I was when I found out that she had run away with that man..."

Suddenly, a pelican landed on the deck moving his huge and deformed peak behind the glass as he observed us. We stopped talking and were contemplating the confused stranger.

"In the letter, Alma says that your pain was known by all and that hers, on the other hand, was secret... what is she referring to?"

"I don't know. She was very shy. I wanted to help her many times. When I got a scholarship and went to college, I wrote to her every month, I sent her dozens of self-improvement books and invitations to courses. I was really concerned about her, but I was never able to decipher the enigma of her isolation. Our childhood was hard. The pain that exists in a household where the father is an alcoholic, and the mother a neurotic, is very deep."

Lisbeth surmised, "You know, I believe I've detected something very serious in her letter..."

"What?"

The pelican flapped clumsily and took off again, heading toward the beach.

"She needs help, urgently."

I looked at the clock. It was six fifteen. The last non-stop flight to Mexico City was at seven o'clock.

I ran to look for the telephone book. I protested out loud when I only found the small local directory. We had been living in that city on the coast for almost two months and I still wasn't used to the distance.

I made a long distance call to my parents' number. Mom answered.

"Hello. It's Zahid, how are you?"

"Well, son, what a pleasure to hear from you."

"Thanks, excuse the rush, but, do you know my sister's address?"

My mother was speechless for a few seconds.

"I have no idea," she finally answered, "since she decided to take off with that man, she's changed a lot. It's been a year since we last saw her. They told me that she had separated from the guy, but I don't know where she could have gone. We've looked for her, but she seems to hide. Have you heard from her?"

I hesitated for a moment... I also had lost track of her.

I remembered that my sister requested in her letter: *"if you can't come to see me, please, don't tell anyone where I am."* That evidently included my parents... But, where could she be? Why hadn't she sent more information so that I could communicate with her? Or was it that St. John's Hospital was so well known?

"Tell me something, Mom," I asked. "Did Alma take with her all the self-improvement books and tapes that I sent to her?"

"No. They're here in the closet if you need them. I honestly don't believe that she even read them. She's very strange..."

Even so, I still loved my sister *exactly the way she was*. Truthfully, perhaps the real reason was I had given her something very valuable of mine.

"Well, I have to go. We'll be in touch. Take care."

As soon as I hung up, I dialed the operator.

The operator took three minutes to pick up the phone; it seemed to me like three hours. When I asked her for information regarding St. John's Hospital in Mexico City, she delayed three more minutes. I cursed her again and again, clenching my teeth. Finally she dictated an address, two telephone numbers and hung up.

Lisbeth was standing as she observed me with a tense look on her face.

"I have the address," I said and anxiously added, "Please, try to call there, see if they know anything about my sister while I change."

My mind was in a whirlwind.

The following week would be the inauguration of my largest company; the main offices had been built in this coastal city, where we had decided to move. If Alma had serious problems, perhaps I wouldn't have enough time to return for the inauguration ceremony. I didn't want to think about that. For the moment I had to pack my briefcase, credit cards, cellular phone, etc... The trip was long, but if we left this same evening maybe everything could be resolved in three or four days and I'd be able to be back in time.

I returned to the living room and listened to Lisbeth talking to someone on the phone.

"What's going on?" I asked.

"They don't want to give me any information over the phone."

"But, do they know about my sister?"

"They said they do."

I grabbed the phone and berated the listener:

"We're on our way but, first of all, tell me. What sort of hospital is it?"

When the blunt and simple voice answered my question, I froze with the confirmation of something that I didn't want to hear.

"Zahid, I've just noticed something else that you're not going to like."

I turned to look at Lisbeth, feeling scared.

"Your sister wrote this letter a *month ago*... She didn't date it, but the stamp shows it. Certainly the company delayed in forwarding it to you, probably waiting until more mail accumulated."

"I'm going to Mexico City. Are you coming with me?"

"Of course."

"But there's no time to pack. The flight leaves in a few minutes."

"I'm ready."

We left the house without turning the lights off. On the way to the airport I drove with my mind lost in memories.

Years back, when I lost my eye, I shared with Alma the lesson I had learned:

We are all called to perfection by *a law that forewarns us.*

NOTHING HAPPENS ALL OF A SUDDEN.

The person who loses his family, who gets divorced, who goes to jail, who ends up alone and without affection cannot say "*this happened to me all of a sudden.*" **We always have gradual warnings until we arrive at the threshold of pain. There are people who react to the simple voice of their conscience or the reading of a book, and there are others who don't want to hear anything and only after they've fallen, do they realize it's time to change.** After suffering the terrible accident to my eye I made a definite decision to succeed in my own transformation. I cried while I explained this to my sister. In her enigmatic letter, now she talked about these same concepts which I had shared with her.

When we arrived at the airport, the lady behind the counter told us briefly that the flight had been closed long before. I told her that it was an emergency, I screamed at her, I almost jumped on the counter wanting to grab her by the hair to make her understand that I was ***not*** asking her if we were on time or not.

"You don't understand," she said to me.

"You are the one who doesn't understand! Stop the damn plane!"

"I'm sorry, Sir. The flight left at six thirty... It's seven o'clock at night."

"Did they change the schedules?"

"Over two months ago."

I felt devastated... it had been more than six months since I had taken a commercial flight.

"Why don't you try to locate the company pilot?" Lisbeth asked me.

"He's not here. Neither is the plane. He went to pick up the special guests for the inauguration."

"We can take an air taxi..."

"Right!"

We ran to the small private aviation building that was located half a mile away.

There was an extremely young and badly dressed pilot on shift that could take us in a small seven seater plane with a pressurized cabin. I calculated. If a jet took three and a half hours, this artifact would take almost six. We would arrive at one o'clock in the morning. Would they let us enter the hospital at that hour?

The other option was to calm down, go back to the apartment and take the ten o'clock flight the next morning. However, one specific paragraph from the letter hammered away at my conscience and made me decide:

I believe that you're one of those who react to the slightest stimulus; one of those who don't wait for greater warnings. I, on the other hand, am one of those who always believe that things will improve by themselves... Now it' s too late...

"We're going."

While they prepared the plane I calmed down. I had gotten down to business. That was the important thing. For the moment, I couldn't do anything else.

"It's going to be a long flight," I said to Lisbeth.

"We can get some sleep. We'll get there first thing in the morning and..." she stopped, "I'm sorry, if you don't want to sleep we can talk. Maybe your nightmares will end when you see Alma."

I nodded.

After a while, we found ourselves walking behind a pilot that did not seem like a pilot, to get on a plane that did not seem like a plane. When we stepped into the passenger compartment, I saw my face reflected in the window. My visual defect was more evident under the yellowish light. Alma thought that I complained each morning because of my mutilation, but human beings can become accustomed to anything and besides, in this day and age, prosthesis can do marvels.

We sat down in the tiny cabin. I took Lisbeth's hand and I said to her, shortly before taking off:

"One day we made a pact that we would not dig into our deepest wounds, that we would not bring up painful memories in order to avoid living through them again, but today the veil has begun to unravel and..."

"It would have happened sooner or later. I told you that it would."

"Will you finish telling me how you overcame your problem with Martin and how you got through an unwanted pregnancy, at seventeen?"

"All right, but only if you tell me the truth about how you lost your eye. And, not superficially or your edited version... I want you to finally open up your heart and let out all the misery you've stored there."

It was a fair agreement. Though still the idea bothered me. She saw me hesitate.

"After you've explained this to me," she insisted, "perhaps you can synthesize your concepts for the inaugural speech. No one gets ahead by chance, Zahid. Each successful man possesses a philosophy about life that leads him to **make the right decisions at the right time**... In summary, that's what you need to tell your personnel."

"To make the right decisions at the right time ." I repeated the phrase that in fact could summarize the essence of success. "It's like pointing to the peak of a mountain and saying: *'Friends, to arrive at the top, just get there...'."*

"Well. The most important thing is how you achieve it. By recalling carefully your own path, you will see how everything clearly comes to the surface."

We were silent while the plane took off, however, with a certain sorrow I reflected how **single mothers tend to be mistreated from the time they're pregnant. "There's nothing more unfair,"** I told myself. **People ignore how mature, how sweet and how kind a woman in this condition can be.**

“I’ll never regret marrying you. I’m proud to be your partner for the rest of our lives.”

After saying this, she softly rested her head on my shoulder. We had only been married four months, however, we couldn’t even imagine that the honeymoon in which we were still living, was about to be tarnished by bitterness.

3

Gradual corruption

I began to speak, remembering the most important parts of the past, although many of them perhaps, Lisbeth already knew. I reclined my seat and closed my eyes in order to better recall the story that I was relating.

At eighteen, I was part of the football team and used to spend hours on the field, I liked to train and longed to become a professional player. However, our team was pathetic and it was difficult to better myself being surrounded by so much apathy. Most of the young men had enrolled in the sport with the sole purpose of avoiding schoolwork. They lacked discipline in their training; their attitude was extremely antagonistic and, because of their fierce and violent threats, the coach was forced to resign. The administration of the school intervened and hired a mature man, excessively strict, in order to get the team back on track. Of the nineteen players, twelve left the team.

One day, Joel, my best friend, and I were walking towards the field when we were intercepted by the group of deserters. They asked us arrogantly where we were going. Neither one of us answered.

“There are seven fags left on the team,” the leader said, throwing his beer can on the ground, in front of me. “Why are they still on the team? Could it be that they like what they do in the showers after training?”

Even though I normally had a volatile temper, this time I didn’t dare challenge the provokers. Joel was the one who answered:

"Leave us alone. We know what we want. You don't."

The offenders let out a laugh and lifted my friend up in the air. Seeing that our integrity was endangered, I yelled:

"You have no right to bother us, we're trying to improve ourselves!"

My innocent reproach added fuel to their flame of contempt. A long list of swear words fell upon us like dense rain. Joel managed to free himself from his oppressors and we both ran away.

We went to the coach and told him what had happened. To a certain degree, we felt proud for having resisted the oppression, but the old man ignored our feat, he didn't even give us a pat on the back or a phrase of support or acceptance. He only punished us for being late by making us do extra push-ups.

I felt let down and hurt. Adults don't realize how they affect the self-esteem of teenagers. It might seem trivial, but the truth is that receiving approval, at that point in my life, was a priority for me. When I got home I told my mom how we had defied the gang, but she also changed the subject. She didn't listen. She wasn't interested. After that, the small wound in my soul began to fester.

We lived in an old three story building. The lower level was used by a video rental business owned by my Uncle Ronispero (who we simply called Ro). We were on the second floor and on the third floor lived my grandmother and our uncle, who was a widower. Ro had always helped support our family, especially after my father became an alcoholic.

Dad changed from being a smart businessman into a sarcastic, temperamental tyrant. He hurt us with his words and sometimes with his hands, and when he got into trouble he blamed others for everything bad that happened. As soon as he arrived home he would pour himself a drink, turn on the stereo, and before he knew it, with the excuse of listening to music, he would consume half a bottle of whiskey.

In a silent conspiracy, we became a team to protect him from his own abuse. When he couldn't get up the next day, mom would call his work and made up an excuse; Uncle Ro would do the shopping and run the most important errands, I would miss school and on occasion, took estimates to his clients. If he vomited on his clothes, we dragged him into his room and changed him. It was a disgusting and depressing task. Sometimes, mother suffered from bouts of depression and locked herself in her room for hours; then Alma was entrusted with the domestic chores and cooked our meals. My little sister believed in her heart that if we all cooperated, dad would somehow stop being an explosive tyrant.

Living with him was like a game of chance. You never knew when he would be ridiculously permissive and when, a cruel abuser. If in sobriety it was difficult to anticipate his reactions, when he was drunk it was impossible. Once he beat me savagely with his belt because I failed a math exam in junior high. My mother was slowly losing her mind; she yelled all the time and was always on edge.

Alma and I learned that there were no limits in our lives other than the mood swings of our parents. Our only peaceful refuge was the upstairs apartment where the advice of Uncle Ro and the prayers of our grandmother partially gave us back our confidence in the human race. Inside the apartment building we went from floor to floor by means of a spiral staircase. More than once I went down to visit my kind uncle and would find my mother crying in desperation, not wanting to call me to help her move and clean my father, who was invariably soiled with his own bowel movements. I didn't know that, just as he couldn't stop drinking due to an addictive compulsion, my mother couldn't leave him for the same reason.

It's a widely known fact today that nine out of ten men abandon their alcoholic wives while nine out of ten women remain with their alcoholic husbands. This isn't because of loyalty.[1] Alcoholism is an evil that addicted husbands **contaminate** their wives with, only it manifests itself in other compulsions. If she doesn't become an alcoholic too, she will become nervous, irritable and dreadfully dependent on their vulnerable relationship, in a maternal yet apprehensive way. This is what happened to my mother.

---

1. Dr. Spickard and Barbara R. Thompson. "Dying for a drink". Vida Editorial, p. 60

Now, after many years, I finally understand that all human beings have EIGHT different attention zones, and that just like my father was *trapped* by an addiction in the PHYSICAL ZONE, and my mother was *trapped* by a psychological obsession in the EMOTIONAL ZONE, I was also *trapped* in the APPROVAL ZONE. I needed desperately to be accepted, loved and wanted. Individuals who are truly appreciated become more productive and have a greater energy for life. One of the cancers of society is the generalized conclusion that demonstrating our appreciation to others *isn't necessary.* We ignore the fact that approval gives us ***self-esteem energy*** and that a person without this energy isn't able to do anything worthwhile. The person who has self-esteem has dignity, character, can face any challenge and remains firm when confronting adversity.

I lacked it all.

Wrapped up in the futile quarreling of my indifferent family, I left football training and renounced my dreams. I suffered a major emotional breakdown, nothing mattered to me except recovering my lost acceptance by others. I didn't want to stick my head out just to have stones thrown at me. I became helpful and condescending to the classmates that had assaulted me, I left the team and joined the gang. I began to dress and wear my hair in the wildest way. Today I know that my change of attitude was one of the worst mistakes of my life.

The camaraderie that I found with the ex-football players was comforting. I realized this for the first time when I went with them to a "rock" concert.

Even before entering the auditorium, I have to confess I felt nervous, as if I were on the verge of crossing into a frontier of unexplored territory. In a certain way, I was.

The place was jammed with teenagers who wore the same kind of "get-ups". The prevailing color was black, jackets, gloves and amulets. The audience displayed wigs, peripheral haircuts on shaved heads, hair hoisted up like tropical palms, painted with psychodelic dyes, fluorescent make up, variegated purple lips, earrings on men and masculine boots on women. A somber fog was cast by the smoke produced by more than a thousand cigarettes.

Suddenly, there was an explosion, a fire on the stage, a deafening noise, and the concert began. In a collective scream, all present got up on their seats and began to scream and clap. The place was flooded with the horrific music of amplified drums and electrical guitars. The music was so loud that the vibrations made the walls shake. The spectators danced and yelled on their chairs. My friends did too. For a while, with my eyes wide open I only watched everyone, but as the hysteria rose and the masses jumped, not on the seats anymore but over the armrests, I began to participate. There were so many people situated aloft, rocking back and forth and screaming, that the natural tendency was to jump as high as possible, both to be able to see the stage, as well as to be a part of the euphoria.

I watched as several bystanders fearlessly struggled to maintain their balance as they climbed onto the backs of their own seats, contorting from side to side until the seat finally broke in two, making the loser fall halfway; I say 'halfway' because there were so many of us and we were so squeezed together, that it was easy to grasp in the air those who had lost their balance and help them stand up again. I could even see how, from hand to hand, over the heads, a girl was transported all the way to the stage, how she kissed the vocalist and how she launched herself with a unique dive into the hands of the audience, who happily returned her back to her spot.

At some point, the lights of the theatre turned off completely and the singing of the crowd filled the black space. The peculiar environment that at first had caused me to feel confused, little by little began to transform into a more familiar and pleasant territory; I found rhythm in the loud noises and the wave of human warmth gradually involved me with its sensation of freedom. It was interesting to observe that everybody danced, sang and jolted each other in a strange way, but no one paid attention to what the one next to them did, no one attacked or lost respect for their neighbors. If you wanted, you could close your eyes, rock back and forth like a lunatic, throw yourself on the floor, do gymnastics or undress... No one cared about the unique way in which you wanted to enjoy yourself. It was as if the most rebellious child in each person had suddenly come alive to release their energies, breaking all the rules. The relaxed atmosphere was contagious. I danced and sang with them, and I felt happy for the first time in many years.

After that event, the members of the gang finally accepted me and I appreciated them more too. I became an active participant in all their meetings and attended all of the concerts that they went to.

I realized that, by changing friends, my way of looking at life had changed too. Before I had thought that to succeed was the most important thing, however now, because of the influence of my gang, it didn't seem that crucial anymore. If years before you had considered it irresponsible to party nightly without inhibitions, now you enjoyed it. **Bad habits are easy to acquire if you're walking downwards into the quicksand.**

At the *beginning*, I felt happy with them, but at the *beginning* I had only perceived things superficially. The fun of "going crazy" night after night goes hand in hand with the irresponsible desire to live without rules, in a fake peace, doing whatever you please, continually. The gatherings' liberal and relaxed environment extended to every aspect of our lives.

Every weekend we organized parties and invited girls from school. The abundance of liquor invariably led us to sex with our classmates. It wasn't until four months had passed when I realized that in all the meetings and some of the parties, marijuana and other types of drugs invariably were present. The peaceful freedom that I had perceived at the first concert was slowly beginning to disappear. My gang demanded that I pay the price of belonging. I tried smoking a 'joint' and went along with them in the most shameless and criminal acts.

It was a gradual and almost imperceptible process of corruption. We stole bottles of wine, robbed cars and assaulted people. We made our hideaway, where we kept the evidence, in an old warehouse filled with rats and spiders.We visited topless bars and on one occasion, excited by the recent show that we had seen, I witnessed our leader violate a young woman, while the rest of us protected him.

I didn't want to involve Ro and my grandmother in the continual deterioration of our family, so I quit visiting them.

One day, I was extremely surprised: my friend Joel approached us, in an attempt to join our clan. When I saw him there, I couldn't believe it. A deep sadness invaded my soul for my friend. When we were both on the football team I believed that Joel would go far; joining us, he was losing his chance to succeed. Yet, I understood him. No one likes to feel alone and even less to be the target of cutting criticism. By joining the other side, I was now free of their cruel attacks and seeing things in this light, Joel was doing the same.

They explained to him that, to acquire their imaginary credential, naturally you had to pass a certain test.

"A beginner's initiation?" he asked, somewhat annoyed.

"Not exactly. It's actually proving to us you've got the guts to lead."

Joel seemed concerned, but he didn't ask any questions. He stood up and went directly to the front as we all left towards the street.

On many occasions, with the excuse of clutching the *banner* of rebellious students, we had stolen buses and used them as private transportation to assault small self-service stores. It seemed foolish to think that we would always get our own way. That night, everything changed.

As a group of twelve, our usual tactic was stopping a bus, entering it yelling, literally making a racket, pushing, slapping and intimidating the passengers while informing them that if they didn't get down immediately, they would regret it. That night, the passengers stood up scared, clutching their belongings and protecting their children, as they hastily retreated by the rear door. The driver, who had given up, asked where we were going and we told him the shopping area. He drove us there directly, but before we abandoned the bus we stole all the money he had earned in fares that day. Normally, the penniless drivers preferred to quickly vanish securing their own safety since the reputation of the student gangs to seek vengeance on those who attempt to get help was widely known, however, this time the driver didn't run away. He parked the bus in the alley and got out to organize an ambush. While we entered the store, he stopped a police car and they called for back up.

Our movements were usually so swift that they had never managed to apprehend any of us. It normally took us an average of fifty seconds to close the door to the store, threaten the cashier and clients, throw down shelves to create confusion, take the money and leave running in different directions.

This time it didn't happen like clockwork.

"The police are coming!" warned the lookout, when we had barely begun.

"Damn!" mumbled our leader, "Joel, take the money in the register and let's go!"

The novice was shaking with fear. The cashier, seeing him hesitate as he approached, punched him in the stomach and Joel doubled over. It all happened so fast. When the crowd was about to start fighting, our leader pulled out a pistol he had been hiding and fired a couple of shots in the air.

Sweating profusely, he put the gun to the manager's head.

"You bastard, you think you're really smart?"

A general apprehension produced by the fear that he would pull the trigger and kill the man, created a deadly silence among the clients and students. Blaring its siren, the first patrol car arrived. The leader grabbed the money that was in sight and darted to the exit. The ones that could follow did; I moved forward, sure of saving my own skin, but an absurd impulse made me stop and go back to help Joel. It wasn't fair that, due to his curiosity, he would be blamed for things he hadn't done. I pulled him up so that he could run with me, but it was too late. Outside, the police managed to catch several of the accomplices. They had their guns pointed at them and were in the process of forcing them to lie down. I searched frantically for another way to escape, pacing through the store like a caged beast, but as soon as I thought about breaking a back window, a policeman came in and stopped us.

We didn't resist.

We were taken to the police station and thrown into filthy cells. I don't know how my friends made out, but half an hour later, two detectives came in to interrogate me.

"We're only students," I insisted, noticing that they were trying to connect us to other crimes in the city.

"Aren't you ashamed, you jerk?" yelled one of them while he belted me across the face. "You insist on showing your student I.D. when you're really a criminal? You aren't students. You're human crap. You don't even have the courage to face what you've done, you're just hiding behind the title of students." He slapped me again. "You've dragged the name and image of real students through the mud. If it were up to me, I would throw you in jail for life and shove your student I.D. up your..."

"Four of them escaped," interrupted the calmer one, "taking the money from the store. If you're in school with them, you must know them well. Where are they?"

I shook my head.

"Don't they sit next to you in ethics class?"

Both of them laughed and, because of my silence, they beat me with such force that I almost fainted...

"And, the only reason I don't smash in your face right now is because the parents of irresponsible losers, idiots, scum like you, tend to sue the police when we mistreat their pretty fags." He looked at the file that he had in his hand. "But I'll do it one day. You're going to turn eighteen next week. You'll be back here again and I swear that when you leave this place next time, no one will recognize you."

When the policemen left, I felt really angry, but not against them, mainly against myself. I knew that everything that they had said was true and, for the first time, it finally dawned on me that, by joining the losers who had deserted the football team, I had committed the most cowardly act of my short existence.

I realized that, to achieve something, anything that's worth the effort, it's necessary to cross the fire of putdowns and mockery. I understood that if I had resisted the attack of those nobodies, perhaps I wouldn't have more than one or two friends, but my spirit would be soaring to the sky... I cursed myself for my lack of character, my weakness, my stupid desire to be accepted by those who it would be better to be despised by...

The authorities urged me to make a telephone call, but I decided not to because I felt worthless and didn't want to cause any more problems at home. If this meant spending several weeks in jail, I'd do it.

"You idiot, you stupid fool!" I kept telling myself, over and over again, while hitting my head against the wall.

4

Associates

Joel did call his father from the police station. He showed up and went through all the bureaucratic red tape in order to obtain his son's freedom. Upon his release, my friend made a gesture that I've always been grateful for. Perhaps recalling that I was there for having gone back to help him, or maybe for the sake of the good times that we spent together trying to make a great football team, he asked his father to pay my bail too.

We got into his father's car and, with a stern look on his face, he drove us impassively towards our neighborhood.

"Where do I drop you off?" he asked coldly.

I answered with a shaky voice. Hearing me weaken, he asked:

"They said the crimes were committed by a gang of teenagers. Do you belong to it?"

I wanted to say that I didn't... that I didn't *anymore*, but it would have sounded phony.

"Yes..." I muttered.

"And you?" he asked his son.

"No."

"Then why did they arrest you?"

Joel threw a furtive look at me and answered with hesitancy:

"I wanted to belong... They're real tough; if you stay on the fringes, they finish you."

"What do you mean?"

"They don't leave you alone, they call you names, they make you look bad in front of others, they make fun of your physical defects and when you achieve something, they jump on you."

"How many are there in the group?"

"Sometimes five, sometimes twenty, but that's not the point. All the kids in our school, guys and girls, support their conduct, they all join in the same game, the atmosphere is very heavy," he paused sounding defeated and childishly declared, "I want to change schools."

Trying to control his anger, his father squeezed the steering wheel and breathed deeply...

"The school is not the problem," he finally said to him. "You're going to find people like that everywhere. You'll encounter the same problem whether you change schools or start a new job. There are many mediocre people; they're the majority and they don't like it when someone else gets ahead. Whatever you do, they'll criticize you, they'll try to make your mistakes stand out, but hardly ever will they acknowledge your accomplishments. Joel, define your goals, fight for them, and if others put you down, don't let it affect you."

"But, if they talk bad about me and I don't say anything, it's almost as if I accept and agree with what they're saying..." he refuted.

"On the contrary. *Explanation not requested means assumed guilt.* He who doesn't defend himself knows that those are lies. Otherwise, he's only throwing a rope around his own neck when he gets angry and answers back the vicious gossip. Everyone thinks: 'if it hurt him that much, it must be true.' Get this through your head. Do you want to succeed? Then, **it's not possible to separate success from the fact you're going to be attacked**. Both come in the same package, but **true success is the result of a lot of hard work, without listening to negative criticism**. Remember, every businessman gets criticized. We always hear false rumors about famous people and the masses love to say that great men are incompetent or that they've been lucky. Thousands of people aspiring for a public career usually give up when they confront their first attack by 'yellow journalism'. Millions of potentially triumphant people have decided to shrug their shoulders and live insignificantly when they've faced the poison of resentful critics. However, poison won't kill you if you don't take it. Let the insults go in through one ear and out the other. If you lower yourself to their same level, you'll stop looking after your own development and you'll be finished, rolling in the muck with them. **Never give in but resist peacefully against the flow. Strive for your dreams and ignore the mockery from the losers. It's part of the price that one has to pay to become someone.**"

From the back seat, I remembered my dream of becoming a great athlete and I couldn't help clenching my fists with anger.

"You can't live isolated from the world either," said Joel.

"**Losers attract losers and there are so many, that they seem to be everywhere, but the winners are also there and in the same way, they tend to associate... Look for them**." Joel's father turned to look at him and realized that he was wearing an earring and a pendant that he hadn't seen before. "What's this?" he asked Joel. "Don't you see? This is an example of what I'm trying to tell you. **Losers ASSOCIATE.** Damn! how I wish I could shake some sense into your head and make you understand this. Innumerable teenagers spend great amounts of time and money seeking acceptance: clothes, hairdos, plastic surgeries, bragging about how much money they spend on cars, sound systems or clothes. These kids are clear proof of their desire to be admired and accepted by others. Stop doing stupid things once and for all. **You're very valuable just the way you are**, tall or short, fat or skinny, dark skinned or fair, you are unique. There's no other human being that has your design and your mission."

"Does that mean I have to accept living without a healthy body, without money, without...?"

"No," he furiously interrupted, "exercise and look after yourself, but stop rejecting your body, your surroundings, your family, your past, your capabilities. Don't you sometimes wish you had more money? Would you let me buy your hand for five million dollars? Will you sell it to me? Stop wasting your time looking for acceptance, and start sowing. *Tomorrow*, you'll only harvest that which you worked for *today*... Nothing is free in life, Joel. Study, improve yourself, plan your life and if they bother you, laugh at them. **You have the right not to be liked by everyone.** Look at it as your right. Learn this by heart: ***No one will ever love you if you aren't capable of taking the risk of some people hating you."***

Joel's father stopped. From where I was, he seemed to be sweating with desperation, as if he were explaining his last will.

Without meaning to or planning it, the lecture was also for me. Later on, Joel confessed to me that his father's explanations and reprimands normally were much less extensive. That night perhaps he was motivated by the fact that he was not only helping his own son.

You have the right not to be liked by everyone.

No one will ever love you if you aren't capable of taking the risk of some people hating you...

"There's an old saying," Joel's father added, "when you hear the dogs barking, it shows someone is walking by..." (Sancho). "Go after your dreams. Listen to the criticism but don't let it hurt you. A statue has never been built for a negative critic. The real transcendental statues belong solely to those who have been criticized. No one triumphs because of their good luck. Those who are jealous will make a lot of noise to attract attention, but in the end, their envy will turn into bitterness and destroy them. The accumulation of all our actions results in who we are today."

"Are you trying to tell me," insisted Joel, "that in order to win one must go *against the entire world*?"

"Don't go to extremes. I'm saying that, **in order to succeed, you must row against the flow of mediocre people who want to see you sink...**"

"But doesn't it seem illogical that, in exchange for being strong enough to stand up against our classmates, we must act like little sheep always obeying our parents?"

"Oh, please! Don't tell me you're really so naive when I know behind that mask there's a very clever person! Have you really become as closed-minded as your friends? Damn! It's not that difficult to understand! You must set your own standards for life, **identify those who want to see you succeed** and join them. I know that teenagers today brag about their freedom and not having to listen to anyone, but **we all obey someone, EVERYONE does. The person who doesn't obey the norms established by society or the family, will then obey his friends' norms or the norms of his own corruption, as a result**

of his depraved and damaging needs... We all obey something," he made a short pause to lower his voice and continued with an air of complicity. "You know that I'm a recovered alcoholic. I began drinking because I didn't know how to say no to the intrusive pressures of my peers. I obeyed them and, before I knew it, my freedom had turned into a prison... Understand this: I'm not only against substances that will always exist like drugs, alcohol or tobacco, but I'm even more against the losers that use them and force others to use them. **Those who insist over and over again that you try something which will injure you, do it consciously or unconsciously in order not to feel alone in their own corruption.** Losers stick together," he insisted, "get away from them and get to work and study, like you did before... **You're what you have between your two ears. Your ideas make you free or a slave. The way you think will give you or take away your energy.** Cultivate your intellect, for your own good."

Joel was silent. I was immobile.

His father arrived at the address I had mentioned and stopped so that I could get out.

"Thanks..." I muttered.

It was then I realized the reprimand was also for me, even though he really didn't know me, because as soon as I opened the door, he looked straight into my eyes and advised me in a very personal and direct way:

"**In order to assure your rehabilitation, a basic rule is to right the wrong you've caused. If you stole something, give it back, if you caused pain, ask for forgiveness; look into your past and repair the damages. Only then will you be able to 'start your life over again'.**"

"Thanks," I repeated, and left the car feeling completely confused.

Deeply affected, Lisbeth stared at me.

It was raining outside. The plane moved abruptly.

"There's one concept that has caught my attention," she said, thoughtfully. "Joel's father told you that both losers as well as winners stick together. Do you realize that this bond is formed thanks to the acceptance that is given? You actually abandoned your football trainer and your family because none of them showed you their appreciation when you needed it and, on the other hand, you joined the gang that did accept you..."

"You're right," I confirmed, "the individuals who accept us turn into our ASSOCIATES and we all end up **looking alike**, in the way we talk, dress or walk and in our goals and habits. A father can feel annoyed at his son and say to him: "*I don't understand why you dress like that, why you speak like that, or why you drink, you've never seen me do that'*. The poor naive adult believes that his son has to be like him only because he is his father, but **the boy *actually* looks like his ASSOCIATES**: those friends who accept him and show him their approval."

"So, in order for a teenager to resemble his relatives, must he feel loved by them?"

"Definitely. The most important fuel that we receive is love, and this is what should fill everyone's emotional tank."

"The **ENERGY OF SELF-ESTEEM**?"

"You memorize everything, don't you?"

She smiled.

"Does our emotional tank ever become empty?"

"Yes. With failures, the energy diminishes a little, with success it increases. It all **depends on the result that we obtain from each ATTENTION ZONE.**"

"Later on, you can explain to me what the 'attention zones' are. For now, let me try to understand it better." Smiling, she paused to think and asked me a tongue twister: "A winner receives, upon winning, more energy, and the loser loses, upon losing, the little energy that he had. Then, how does a loser recover the lost energy in order to begin winning like the winner?"

I laughed at her play on words and answered in the same way:

"Listening to new ideas and committing oneself to the positiveness of these concepts."

Her sweet laugh bubbled out.

"But isn't it wrong that the energy people need only increases by **acceptance and performance**?"

"In the beginning it increases like that, but as we gain more and more fuel, we also acquire **RESERVES.**"

Tenderly, she watched me with her round eyes while listening avidly.

"Then, **the better I act and the more acceptance I receive,** the more *energy reserves* I'll have in my tank?"

"Yes, **the RESERVES turn into your own unquestionable convictions, into a philosophy of life; a certainty of being worthy; the pride of being alive; for being a child of God; for being loved by Him. The RESERVES offer dignity and self-respect. In a mature person they are unalterable even if he no longer possesses the same *performance and acceptance* that he had before.**"

"That's interesting," she said, "but, please, don't go off on another tangent and tell me what happened next."

I felt flattered by her growing interest and continued my narration exactly where I had left off.

I got out of the car and wandered the dark streets. The neighborhood was practically deserted. Suddenly, I realized I was close to the old warehouse where the gang used to hide their drugs and stolen goods. I checked out the abandoned building, consumed with revenge, frustration and guilt; three negative emotions that I didn't know how to control. I approached the building and, after making sure no one was there, I sneaked in through the secret door. I immediately found the hidden stash and money from recent robberies. I wanted to challenge the gang and at the same time I wanted to make amends for the damage by returning the money that I had helped steal... Being there, my mind was flooded with nightmares of the past, the ridicule, the taunting, the pressure to conform to the gang and the sad nostalgia for having abandoned my own dreams. All of that, combined with the frustration of being a neglected son, being sick of my family, as well as the deception I felt when I realized what was really behind the 'rock' concerts, made me lose my head as I stormed into everything, full of pent up rage.

My movements were not coherent or lucid.

A blinding wrath made me knock over the table that we used at our meetings. I kicked it and, as if I was possessed by a legion of demons, I began to break everything in sight. After a while there wasn't a single object left. All that was possible to destroy was destroyed, but my fury was so intense that I wasn't satisfied yet.

I looked for the lighter that we used to smoke marijuana. Then, I piled the drug into the center of the dark room and set it on fire.

A dense and foul smoke began to fill the place.

So they wouldn't know who had done it, before I left I wrote some obscenities on the wall and, after taking a hammer from the warehouse, I snuck out by the secret alley and broke the old rusty padlock on the main door. That way, my ex-comrades would believe that another gang had forced the door and found our secret gold mine.

Yet, how strange human nature is! The same mind that had been reflecting minutes before, now could not foresee what was before his very own eyes: that by filling his pockets with the stolen money and the evidence of what he had destroyed, would be like tying a rope around his neck, almost condemning himself to death.

I made sure that I had the money in my pockets as I ran away. The smell from the smoke coming out of the building would soon catch someone's attention and the fire department would be alerted. I smiled triumphantly. If that happened, my ex-friends would never know who had caused the destruction.

Far away, I stopped running and began to whistle, ignoring what destiny had waiting for me.

It was almost one o'clock in the morning and logically I thought everyone would be asleep at home, but I was wrong. I was just going up the stairs to the first floor when I heard a racket from our building. I stopped, feeling confused and tried to confirm if in reality, the laughter, clapping and whistling was coming from my apartment. There was no doubt. As I took out the key, my hand was shaking and some of the bills fell out of my pocket. I quickly picked them up, holding them tightly in my fist and shoved them back into my pants pocket. Afraid of what I might find when I opened the door, I turned the key very slowly, as I broke out in a cold sweat.

I was so cautious that the noisy party-goers didn't see me when I entered. The scene that I encountered was shocking: My father with three friends had organized a real drunken orgy. They were so plastered that they didn't realize how ridiculous they really were. Their shirts were scattered all over the place. An obese guy, without pants and covered only under his punch by some dirty underwear, danced in front of the others imitating the voluptuous movements of a cabaret dancer. Dad and two more drunks applauded and whistled at him.

I froze at the door. And my mother? and my sister? How could this gross disorder be going on in our home while they slept? Had they fled to the apartment upstairs, or were they frightened hiding in their bedrooms without being able to sleep? I was standing there with my mouth wide open, when dad noticed me. Greeting me loudly, he stumbled towards me and grabbed my sleeve, forcing me to join his party.

5

Attention zones

I made a long pause in my story.

"What are you thinking about?" asked Lisbeth, seeing me suddenly quiet.

"The problems in my family were complex, but they wouldn't have seemed so overwhelming if I had known the concept of the '*attention zones*'. Without this knowledge, I was unescapably drawn into a whirlwind."

"All right," she said, giving up, "that idea about the 'zones' has been on your mind for a while. Why don't you explain it to me?"

"Are you really interested in talking about it?"

"Yes. As long as you finish telling me about the past, later on, exactly how it happened."

"I promise," I accepted. "All human beings possess EIGHT AREAS that we look after, consciously or unconsciously, during the twenty-four hours of each day and for our entire life. We are the result of **multiplying the attention zones that we CHOOSE by the TIME we invest in them.** It really isn't feasible to estimate the personal improvement of anyone without first understanding this concept. It's important because it provides us with a clear picture of the position we're in right now and it also explains the way in which we neglect the other zones if we become trapped in one."

I closed my eyes and recalled the charts that I had written one night, shortly after finishing college. I had spent many years analizing them, until they had taken shape and had become clear and concise. I meticulously defined them to my wife as if describing a map of lost treasure.

FIRST. PHYSICAL ZONE

The method for survival is found in this zone, and it must be looked after daily. We do so as we eat, drink, urinate, defecate, breath, sleep, exercise, practice our sexuality or bathe. The procedure can "break down", leaving the person sick with a disease or trapped in bad habits such as gluttony, laziness, alcoholism, drug addiction, etc. Any physical problem *compels* us to devote much more time to this attention zone, thus neglecting and breaking down the consequential mechanisms of the other zones.

SECOND. EMOTIONAL ZONE

We are in this zone when we experience strong emotions such as *joy, rage, fear, depression or passion.* We also find ourselves in this area when we pause to calm our nerves, to meditate or rest. We are trapped in it when we have psychological compulsions or uncontrollable emotions such as resentment, envy, desires for revenge, jealousy, worry, guilt, sadness, anger, euphoria, passion or fears.

THIRD. APPROVAL ZONE

When we are in this zone, we decide to behave in a certain way in order to feel accepted, admired and loved by others. For example: an adolescent will spend long hours trying to begin a romance and will allow his studies to become secondary. However, this isn't because he loves someone but because he needs to feel loved. At first, the human being doesn't know how to love. He has to learn. It's a great lie to say: *no one can be loved if he doesn't give love. In reality, no one can give love without having received it first.*

An example of this is when a lack of approval makes a tyrant threaten others. He is constantly instilling fear and thus <u>forces</u> them to belong to his group.

FOURTH. PREVENTIVE ZONE

You look after this zone by obtaining material goods, seeking economic resources for your safety and future stability, as well as by defending your patrimony and yourself from the abuse of others. This procedure "breaks down" when you lose your perspective and start looking at everything with materialistic eyes; when we become stingy and greedy workaholics, even stealing or fighting over money.

"Furthermore, there are FOUR other zones designated as superior," I explained, enthusiastically, "those are the most important ones, since they constitute the highest goals all human beings should aspire to reach. When we look after the SUPERIOR ZONES we forget time, money and applause and we don't even pay attention to our simplest physical needs."

Lisbeth listened to me attentively. I took a pen and a business card out of my briefcase and sketched a chart in order to explain it better:

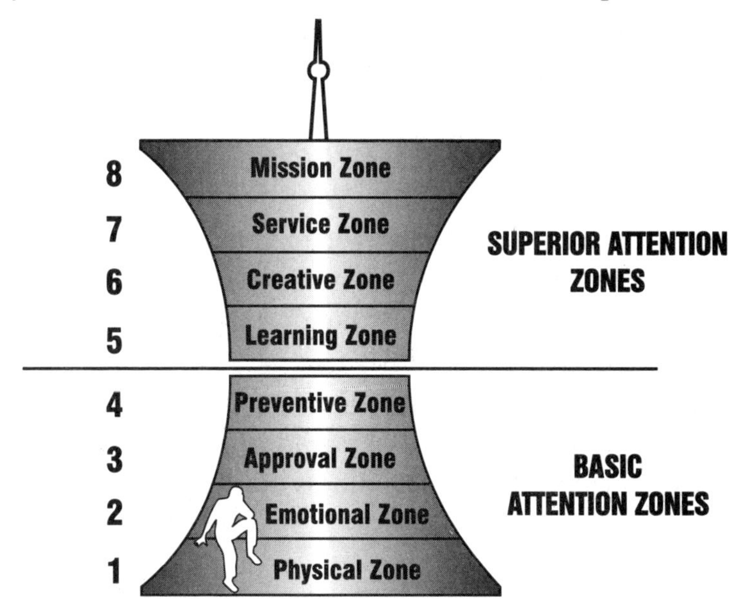

I described the second group of zones very carefully, indicating each step with my pen:

SUPERIOR ATTENTION ZONES

FIFTH. LEARNING ZONE

In this zone, we must understand that the first reason for living is TO IMPROVE ourselves and that, in the end, we are in this world for the same reasons that a student goes to college. We nurture this zone when we read, listen, observe, take notes, study, experiment, investigate and write essays, always with the purpose of becoming better.

SIXTH. ZONE OF CREATION

As a human being we're created in the image and likeness of our Creator, precisely because He has the ability to create. The person who never develops this capability will never be a complete human being. When a task becomes exciting it's because something new is being CREATED, such as writing, painting, composing, building models, weaving, decorating, constructing, designing, inventing new systems, undertaking projects or any activity which in itself, stimulates creativity.

SEVENTH. ZONE OF SERVING

Love is experienced here. We enter this zone when, "to be the first, means to be the last and to voluntarily be the servant of all"[1]; when we think about the needs of others and lend a helping hand; listening to the lonely; comforting those who are sad and offering support to the little man who is looking up to us for help; teaching others what we know, encouraging them to grow, showing them the way; looking after our children and family, always seeking first the happiness of our partner.

EIGHTH. MISSION ZONE

When we reach the highest level in life, we clearly understand we are alive for a reason, that we have a mission to fulfill at this exact time and place, precisely where we are, with our special talents and shortcomings... The sense of mission is implicitly bound to our personal relationship with God, to the certainty that He expects something from us, and with the personal conviction that there is a spiritual life after this one on earth, where the person who has been given more talents will be demanded to account for more... A person in this zone turns into a brilliant human being, whose life has a superior meaning.

My wife nodded, completely absorbed, trying to assimilate all the information.

"You're right. It is a very stimulating topic," she said, "but tell me something. Can I look after several zones at the same time?"

"No. You can go from one to another quickly, but you can only be in one at a time."

"Then, for example, if I find myself performing a job to earn money (preventive zone), but I do it with creativity (creative zone), am I not at the same time in two different zones?"

"No. You started in one and ended up in another. At the beginning you thought only about your payment, but as soon as you started to ***create***, to project yourself, you forgot the money and would even do it ***for free***, since you ***advanced*** to the 'zone of creation' and your efforts became so valuable you don't even consider their monetary worth."

"Creative acts don't have a price... this point fascinates me," confessed Lisbeth, "it gives me a good reason to continue painting. Even though I don't get paid and people say that I'm wasting my time."

"Of course. However, study the chart. **In order to CREATE, one must advance through the first step which is to LEARN**. In fact, these two zones are closely related. A musician can only fully enjoy his moments of creation after paying the price of practicing his instrument for many years... **The quality of any creative work is intimately bound by the amount of time invested in learning about one specific field.** Thus, almost anyone would be able to create works similar to Da Vinci, Michael Angelo or Einstein, ***if that person were willing to pay the price of constantly being in the process of creating and learning."***

Lisbeth observed me with an astonished look.

"Incredible..." she muttered and stared into space for a while. "Then, does this show us a human being's priorities?"

"Yes. When you have **a problem in a basic zone it's very difficult to look after a superior one**. For example, a sick child (*physical zone*), sad or scared (*emotional zone*), will NOT be able to listen to his teacher at school (*learning zone*)."

"Or a country without money or without minimal safety conditions (*preventive zone*), will NOT be able to think in terms of peace or love (*zone of serving).*"

"Exactly. That is the reason why the drawing has the shape of an hourglass in which the path narrows exactly in the middle. Most of the people live trapped in the narrow area. They go down easily, but it takes them a lot of work to rise. On the top, the route is broadened again because men have learned to live **not only** in their own strengths, but in those of God."

"How might it have helped you at that time to know about the attention zones?"

"In the same way in which a map can help someone that is lost in a great city to locate his position and to visualize where he must go."

She watched me for a few more seconds without speaking. Suddenly she startled into reality and urged:

"Now, can you continue telling me what happened to you?"

I nodded. After all, I had promised her.

After the botched robbery, the short term incarceration, the punches from the policemen, the reprimand from Joel's father and, above all, after having made enemies with the same hoods that months back I had insisted on being friends with, I arrived at my house in a state of tremendous turmoil. However, as soon as I went in, the *energy from my self-esteem* was abruptly switched off. As if a superior power had taken the batteries away from me, I remained trapped in the sick emotions of an alcoholic's son.

My father took me to the center of the party:

"I want to introduce to you the first-born of this family," he said, lifting his index finger and pointing at my nose as if he intended to lean on it.

I couldn't avoid the look of disgust that swept over my face. In addition to material goods (which are the least important), children inherit habits, ideas, religion, levels of self-esteem, predisposition to addictions and many other fundamental patterns of behavior. Certainly, for Alma and me, our inheritance didn't make us the luckiest of siblings.

"This boy," continued Dad, with the irregular intonation of a drunk, "plays football and has the most muscular legs that you've ever seen."

The guy across the room changed chairs and sat down putting his arm around me. He began speaking with his fat lips covered with saliva, so close to my face I could smell his foul breath.

"It's a pleasure to meet you. Your father always talks about you," the drunkard hiccuped and belched in my face. "Hey, guys, get this young man a drink!"

Dad tried to pour whiskey into a glass, but after only a few drops, the bottle was empty.

"Where's another bottle?" he screamed banging the bottle against the coffee table.

"Are we going to keep on dancing?" questioned the naked clown with the dirty underpants, who was still waiting to receive more applause and continue his grotesque pantomime.

"Why are you taking so long?" angrily huffed Dad, demanding more booze.

Who was he talking to? I turned around. With all the noise, it seemed unthinkable that my mother could be asleep, but it wasn't logical either to suppose that she was awake serving this debauchery. I was wrong in my second calculation. When mother appeared, I felt a direct blow to my heart. She seemed like a madwoman. She approached slowly and stiffly, with her eyes wide open. The half-naked guy didn't make the slightest attempt to cover himself. She picked up the glasses and mumbled fearfully that there wasn't any more liquor.

"Then think of something! Bring beer or brandy or whatever you've got!"

"I told you that there isn't anything."

My father grabbed her by the apron and dragged her violently towards him.

"If you don't get something, I swear that we'll go somewhere else, where they treat us better."

The sanest answer seemed to be to tell him to leave but, by doing this, she would be creating an even greater problem. Certainly, as soon as they left, the four drunks would be stopped by the police, would get lost or suffer a serious accident, the most obvious being to fall down the stairs.

My mother left the room and, after a few minutes, she returned with half a bottle of rum. Dad grabbed it from her without saying anything. He poured a little more into my glass and handed it to me.

"Be a man!"

I drank a sip feeling nauseous.

"Bottoms up!"

I blindly obeyed. Dad had a strong psychological dominance over me. He inhibited my self-will. He intimidated me. You could never anticipate his next reaction. To question his orders could provoke either a merciless beating or one of his usual crying jags, threatening to commit suicide.

The drunken clown with the yellowish underwear wanted to do a cartwheel but lost his balance and fell on his face.

"Let the boy dance!" suggested one of the drunkards, watching the comedian collapse. The other three applauded and began to whistle. My father compelled me to get up and ordered:

"Show them your football player legs and give us a demonstration of your workouts!"

I stood up stiffly, embarrassed to take even a step.

"Come on, don't be so shy. Show these fat drunks what it is to have strong muscles."

I remained silent, trapped in the *emotional zone,* prisoner of a deep humiliating shyness.

Dad seized me by the waist and suddenly pulled down my pants. When he did this, all the money that I had in my pockets fell at his feet.

"What's this?"

I didn't answer.

"Did you steal it?"

I bent down to gather the money and, when I did, a stupid impulse made me speak without considering the consequences:

"Yes. I haven't played football for some time, but I steal at night."

Suddenly and without any warning to protect myself, he lifted his leg straight up and kicked me in the face. I fell on the floor with my eyes closed, seeing in the blackness of my eyelids hundreds of yellow lights glittering.

My dad picked up the money, mumbling that he hadn't taught me criminal habits like that; that maybe he sometimes drank but had never robbed and that in his house you could be anything but not a thief. (Those were hollow words without any meaning because, since he took the money, or should I say, stole it, I've never seen it again.)

When I opened my eyes, I saw Alma's shadow in the hallway, watching me. She was crying, contemplating the living nightmare. She was the sole stimulus that gave me a little bit of energy. Leaving my father busy picking up the money, I started crawling with my pants around my ankles. As soon as I left the danger zone, I stood up, took my little sister's hand and stumbled every step of the way to her bedroom. We locked the door, I put my pants back on and we hugged each other desperately. I caressed her head, I wanted to ask her forgiveness, to say to her that I wouldn't let him do this to her, but I couldn't speak. I only held her and wept. She stepped back to look at my split and purple lip and opened the door to go and get me a bag of ice, but at the same moment she ran into my mother who was approaching, ready to vent her spleen.

"Why did you come home so late?" she asked.

"We were at a party."

"And the money?"

"It's a friend's. He gave it to me to keep."

"What an ingrate you are! You see how much I suffer with your father and, instead of helping me, you're out in the streets like a bum. I'm glad you can see how terrible things are in this house. You're completely insensitive. Doesn't anything matter to you? Don't you see that I'm a woman and that I'm sick? Can't you try to get home early to help? Your poor sister is the only one that helps me," she paused to wipe her forehead as if she were a martyr and added: "If something really horrible happens, you'll be responsible."

Her words hurt me more than the blow from my father. I didn't realize that my mother was losing her mind due to the uncontrollable pressure of having to put up with an alcoholic husband. I just looked down, feeling the poison seeping bitterness into my soul.

---

[1] The Holy Bible - Mark 9:35

6

Alcoholism and closed-mindedness

That night I slept with a chair blocking the door. Did I say, sleep? I only lay in bed, listening to the noises outside, thinking that anytime, my new enemies would arrive to claim the money that I didn't have anymore. I recalled the words of Joel's father: "*You're what you have in your mind. Your ideas will make you free or a slave. The way that you think takes away or gives you energy*". Trying to doze while my sweaty body still trembled, I reflected I'd have to read a lot of books. It wasn't an option to escape the quicksand, it was an unavoidable and imperative obligation. My eyes were wide open as I stared at the ceiling. My God! I suddenly remembered something that could save me from the oncoming tornado. During his lenghty reprimand, Joel's father had mentioned that he was a *recovered alcoholic!*

As soon as the sun came up, I showered and snuck out of the house. I had to walk through the disaster area where it looked like a bomb had gone off. There were bottles thrown on the floor, furniture everywhere, the smell of liquor and disgusting drunks who were sprawled all over with their legs askew and snoring out loud. I could have easily emptied the pockets of my disgraceful father in order to recover the money, but I preferred to escape instead. I needed to see my friend's Dad to ask him for guidance; to beg him for advice; to have him explain to me the concepts that make you free; to ask him to share with me this new way of thinking that gives you energy.

I arrived at Joel's house at seven thirty. I paced back and fourth in front of the door without daring to knock. Finally I sat on the sidewalk and waited. At eight o'clock in the morning the electrical garage door opened and his car came out.

I stopped him imploring for help, explaining how much I had thought over everything he had told me and that I didn't want to be with the wrong crowd anymore.

"Teach me," I begged, "what do I have to do?"

The man looked impatiently at his watch.

"Start studying and get to work." he said to me. "Get rid of your lazy excuses and begin to help others. That's the gist of what I can advise you right now."

He put the car in reverse and I moved back.

"Sir," I insisted, raising my hand. "My problem is urgent. Please, help me..."

"Look for me in the evening," he said, activating the remote control to make the door close and putting the car in drive, "right now, I'm in a hurry."

"My father is an alcoholic!" I yelled after him. As I watched the car leave, a depressing letdown enveloped me.

I lowered my head, full of frustrated hope. I simply stood there for a while, then, trying to release my disappointment, I kicked a rock before turning around to leave. All of a sudden, I saw the car appear on the opposite side of the street, as if he had second thoughts and decided to return by going around the block.

He stuck his head out of the window and glared at me.

"Your father is an alcoholic?"

I nodded, stammering and confused as I began to disconnectedly relate what had happened at my house the night before.

"Get in the car. Ride with me to work and we'll talk on the way."

I ran around the car and jumped in next to him.

"Now, do you understand why I was so furious last night?" he asked. "Anyone can get sucked into the trap on the way down."

"Yes," I said rapidly. "My father was the sales manager of a food company. He earned an award for his innovative ideas and achieved the best performance record, but he's gone down hill. He's turned into an unpredictable person. My sister and I are desperate and deeply hurt because of everything that he's done to us."

The driver remained silent for a long while. His sight was fixed ahead. Perhaps he was thinking about the times he had caused similar damage to his own family.

"And you, how did you kick the habit?" I asked putting the finger right on the sore without beating around the bushes anymore.

"Alcoholism is never cured. I'm rehabilitated but, even today, after more than ten years of being sober, if I overestimate myself, I could have a relapse where I would never recover. The alcoholic must always live on the alert, carefully keeping his own vital score and always be conscious of his vulnerability."

"But then, why does alcohol..." I asked, anxious to understand all at once thousands of things which were still mysteries to me "produce such terrible aftereffects if it's something created to make people happy?"

Joel's father smiled with bitterness.

"Alcohol is **not** made to stimulate good humor, in reality it's a depressant. It freely crosses the walls of the digestive system and fifteen seconds after having been ingested, it enters the blood stream, thus intoxicating the brain and slowing down its operation, to put it more simply, it anesthetizes the brain. It numbs the part that stores the information on inhibitions, so the person feels free of restrictions, relaxed. At the same time, the drug impairs his intellectual capacity and ability to react correctly to stimulus, reducing his reflexes, reasoning and memory."

"But, in greater doses it's worse than that, isn't it?"

"In large quantities, alcohol depresses the cerebellum affecting the balance mechanism. In much greater measures it attacks and anesthetizes the rachidian bulb which regulates vital functions like breathing and the heart. Many teenagers die of a respiratory spasm after having binging contests with their friends (drinking a full bottle without stopping). On the other hand, there's evidence that each time the cerebral neurons are inhibited, hundreds of them die... The following day, a drinker wakes up with a headache, but doesn't realize that his intellectual capacity has diminished, maybe by a thousandth. The body starts adapting to the intoxication, thus acquiring dependency. After years have passed, the loss of mental aptitude is more obvious and perhaps by then, other complications have surfaced, such as cancer, hepatic cirrhosis, gastric ulcers, as well as occupational, marital and parental problems."

I was surprised that a recovered alcoholic would give me all of this information.

"And s... sir," I stammered, "excuse me, what is your name?"

"It's Joel too, like my son's."

"Excuse me, Don Joel. Is it common to get addicted slowly?"

"Of course, why?"

"Because I don't know how my father became an alcoholic. All of his life he was proud of his knowledge about wines and liquors but rarely did he get drunk. Without him realizing it, he kept increasing the dose. Does dependency always increase *gradually* and *obliviously*?"

"Sometimes. It all depends on the genetics and metabolic conditions of the individual. Some become addicted very quickly while others, like your father, take many years for the cycle to close. The process, slow or fast, almost always follows the same pattern. First you start as a **SOCIAL DRINKER**, that is, ***drinking at parties or with friends***. Once that you experience the sensation of well-being, you become a **RELIEF DRINKER**, this is a person that ***looks for a drink, alone, in order to feel relief from his pressures.*** From this level to the next, there is only one step, the person acquires tolerance (the person needs larger doses to achieve the same effects than before) and then, he has become a **GREAT DRINKER**, ***someone who can drink larger amounts without feeling 'high', someone who feels proud of being able to drink longer and control alcohol at his will.*** Being a great drinker is the vestibule to alcoholism, the membrane that separates both phases is too thin to know where one ends and the other begins."

"My father was both a *social* and *relief* drinker for over twenty years. A whole lifetime without becoming addicted, do you know what I mean?"

"Sure. That's very common. That's why the **average** family takes *seven years* of facing the evidence to admit that there is an alcoholic at home, and *two more years* to seek help."[1]

As reality set in, my eyes opened wider with surprise. Seven plus two, nine years of living in hell without doing anything about it. I made a mental count. It was true. It had been eight for us.

"The picture you describe is terrible," I said, with a sour taste in my mouth, "but there's still something that I don't quite understand. I always thought that a well educated person, who knows how to drink, is free from that danger. How can someone with my father's intellectual level and maturity fall into such an addiction?"

"The connoisseur of 'fine' wines seeks its pleasant taste or uses it with the excuse of helping improve digestion, but for some it's very easy to lose focus. There's no one, do you understand? no one that is exempt from the risk of falling into an addiction. **It doesn't depend on your willpower**, but on overestimating yourself, 'handling snakes' and bragging that they will never bite you. The drug starts becoming a friend to your organism. It lives like a pleasant pet which the more you feed, the more it grows, but that will attack you when you least expect it. Your emotional situation, age and physical condition are changing elements that allow alcohol different inroads in your daily life, until it finds the ideal one to attack. **It's not the specific properties of a substance which make it addictive, but the COMBINATION of those properties with the chemical condition found in each particular individual.** The genetic factor is important but not the only one. Neither doctors, psychiatrists, nor fortune tellers can predict when the **internal conditions** will allow the animal's rage to awaken and, when this happens, the person's addiction worsens quickly. The sickness can be disguised. **You don't need to be lying in the streets to have a problem; only five percent of addicted drinkers live on the streets.**[2] The rest of them are our neighbors, lawyers, doctors, psychologists, sales people, teachers, business people who we see walking out of their homes every morning, showered and well dressed, but no one knows the internal torture that they may be living. They don't even acknowledge it themselves. Frequently, they only think that they are moody. A recovered alcoholic that I once met shared with us, in his testimony, that for him it was torture to work as a dentist. At his office, he couldn't think about anything else. The desire turned into an almost physical presence that took away his concentration. He felt sick, nauseous, and only when he had a drink did he feel better and could think about other things. If he made a supernatural effort, he could stay away from drinking for several weeks and when everything seemed that it was going to be easy, the desire came back even stronger and more uncontrollably than ever."

This same problem was very similar to my family's case. At the beginning, Dad went through a similar struggle. He didn't get drunk every day, he went for days, sometimes months, without drinking a drop of alcohol, but then, all of a sudden he would start again.

"When the animal has matured inside of you," continued Don Joel, "it frequently behaves cunningly, it seizes your insides, vigilant, breathing patiently, waiting without any rush for the right moment to carry out its objective, to kill you...The addiction really has its own life. It's like a cancer that has awakened, taking control away from the affected person. Today, 8 to 15 million workdays are lost every year due to alcohol. According to data from WHA[3], close to 10% of the world's population is alcoholic. In Europe, most of the people consider alcohol as an indispensable complement for meals, even though for many, it gets out of control and even though 10% of all deaths are due to this drug. In many countries, 30 to 50% of the patients in psychiatric hospitals require alcoholic rehabilitation. At the XXXII World Health Assembly, alcoholism was declared to be one of the major public health problems in the world."[4]

I felt furious not knowing exactly why. How was it possible that television promoted and used strategies to convince young adults that sporting events or parties weren't 'cool' without booze?

"And why, if it's such a threatening drug, isn't it forbidden like opium or marijuana?" I asked.

"Alcohol is a LEGAL DRUG for three reasons. *First:* the addiction that it creates has been inherited since the beginning of history, from one generation to the next. ***Second:*** the number of addicts is so frightfully high that if it were prohibited (this has been tried at different times), drinkers would turn this world upside down. ***Third:*** it is one of the most lucrative businesses on earth. A high percentage of national funds is supported by the taxes from their sales. Hundreds of thousands of families live directly or indirectly from the revenues produced by this multimillion dollar industry."

"Television commercials are *selling* something completely different," I said, thinking out loud.

"It's true. To sell it 'legally' they have to give a deceiving misinterpretation to the real image. The marketing experts make people believe that drinking gives a certain status, that certain liqueurs are symbols of good taste, culture and breeding. Beer is related to sports; whiskey, to elegant reunions; mixed drinks to parties and youthful romance... When some experts talk about the wine culture, they emphasize their digestive qualities and sincerely consider liquor as an indispensable and irreplaceable delicacy. However, the truth is that **alcohol is present in the majority of assaults, car accidents, rapes, sexual abuse and mistreatment of children, spouse beatings, family disintegration, divorces, street fights, besides the fact that it's justifiably called the ENTRY DRUG.**"[5]

"Something like the door to other drugs?"

"Exactly. Normally, people start drinking alcohol before consuming any other type of major narcotics."

"How strange when it's really a drug too; yet alcohol consumption is viewed with acceptance."

"Well, if cocaine, for example, were advertised on television, if it were within our children's reach, if it were sold at the corner store and we were all forced to accept a little 'sniff' at every party or reunion, you can be sure too that cocaine addicts would be seen with more accepting eyes."

"But alcoholism is a *disease* in itself, isn't it?"

"Of course. A PROGRESSIVE one because the affected person, even if he has periods of lucidity that seem to give quite a bit of hope, in reality, gets worse everyday, and MORTAL because if he doesn't get help in time, he will invariably end up dying because of his habit."

"Is it something like diabetes or cancer?"

"Alcoholism is **much worse than any other disease**. Normally, when an individual suffers from heart problems, diabetes or cancer, he keeps his circle of significant and loving relationships, his home, his material goods and his friends whilst the alcoholic, commonly loses everything. The suffering is not only physical, it's above all spiritual, mental and family related. It hurts everyone that lives with the person, kills his supportive relationships, destroys his intellect and means of economic sustenance."

"Tell me, how did you become rehabilitated?" I asked again, stuck on the idea.

Don Joel pulled the car to the side, reducing the speed.

"Only when I realized that I was sick and fell on my knees, asking forgiveness for all the times that I had attacked others, did I begin to recover."

"Asking for forgiveness?" I laughed openly, and my laugh was sincere. "You don't know my father."

"You're the one who doesn't understand alcoholics. The real tragedy is that the sick person **doesn't accept that he needs help**. Perhaps he might go to the doctor to complain about headaches, night sweating, depression, digestive problems, etc. etc., but he won't acknowledge that he has drinking problems."

I thought my father fitted this description perfectly, but so did my mother.

"With the same train of thought," I said, "many people never recognize their mistakes and **believe that everything is someone else's fault.** I live surrounded by people like that. My family's problems are a complicated maze without an exit."

Don Joel stopped the car and directed his accusing eyes right on me.

"Get this straight, once and for all," he emphasized. "Your father has **TWO** DIFFERENT and independent SICKNESSES. They seem to be one and, frequently, we make the mistake of getting them mixed up but, in reality, **there are two**: **ONE** is ***alcoholism***, and **THE OTHER** is ***closed-mindedness***. The majority of those who suffer from alcoholism, also suffer from *closed-mindedness*, but not the opposite way. Millions of people suffer from *closed-mindedness* without being alcoholic."

I couldn't help feeling stunned. I felt as if my mind was one huge question.

"What sicknesses are you talking about?"

"***Closed-mindedness*** is formed by a series of symptoms that appear when the EGO becomes sick. It's not a medically registered name but I hope that one day soon, it will be; because the truth is that it's a psychological illness. Just like there are neurotics, schizophrenics and paranoiacs, there are also ***'closed-minded people'***; persons with a chronic hardhead, is that clear? **An increase in conceit and authoritarian whims** are the first symptoms."

He then put the car in drive and slowly eased back unto the freeway.

We stopped at a traffic light and he turned again to look at me.

"**The *closed-minded* person, no matter what his age, has an archaic mind. It's the sickness of the stagnated brain. They think they've seen it all and know it all; they're arrogant, narcissistic braggers who thrive on pointing out everyone else's mistakes; they get irritated if someone gives them advice; and when someone criticizes them, they react ferociously.** Such is the case of apprehensive mothers who spend all of their time correcting the women around them because they believe they exclusively possess the secret to children's health; or is also the case of men who imagine aggressions from other drivers and jump out of their cars challenging them to fight. They're obnoxious people who think they own the world and have the right to lecture everyone, as well as educate and eliminate the stupidities of others. They manipulate and intimidate anyone who thinks differently from them; always minimizing other people's success, bragging they could have done it better."

"Looking at it like that," I objected, "we are all a little *closed-minded*."

"Yes, just like we're all a little bit neurotic, using different defense mechanisms depending on the circumnstances. However, there are normal and abnormal levels. When the neurosis or *closed-mindedness* grows and becomes chronic, the person is NOT HEALTHY ANYMORE. **This sick person softens the hearts of the people that are close to him and pushes them to believe that they're guilty of his mistakes.** He has a great ability to make others feel badly by pointing out their faults and attacking them with destructive criticism. Afterwards, when the same people feel overwhelmed, he then turns sweet and tender, creating emotional confusion. Many *closed-minded* people reject any relationship with God and make fun of those who are spiritual, labelling them as naive and sanctimonious. Others, on the contrary, are extremely religious and with their book of rules in hand, condemn and judge others feeling as if they were 'the fourth person of the Trinity'. Those who are involved with the *closed-minded*, think that by being the way that he wants them to be and by putting up with his bad moods, everything will change; that is why, intimidated, they prefer not to alter the calm, to remain quiet and to keep indulging his egocentric whims. Thousands of wives of these *closed-minded* men take over the responsibilities that their husbands drop; they justify and protect their tyrant, also closing their minds and, in a way, becoming just as sick as he is."

"That's my mother," I interrupted.

The driver behind us impatiently honked his horn trying to make us move since the light had already turned green.

"The children and spouses of *closed-minded people*," he said, starting the car again, "feel trapped in a dead end and frequently try to escape the problem through addictions and even through suicide. In one study, 75% of teenagers that commit suicide, are the children of alcoholics. In another one, the number went up to 90%."

The driver that was behind us passed our car while yelling obscenities and honking his horn.

"But many times," I replied, "the relatives are waiting for the sick person to '***hit rock bottom***'. They say that only then will he react and realize that he has a problem."

"That's a ridiculous myth. The person who has ***'hit rock bottom'*** has damaged his entire world and has nothing more to lose. For this reason, it's almost impossible to rehabilitate him. The most vital support a sick person can have in order to recover is a family, a job, friends or a home to protect."

I thought about his words without saying anything. Today, after many years, I'm sure that what he defined so accurately as *closed-mindedness*, is **the typical attitude obstructing the entrance to the *superior zones of attention*.** In order to be able to rise to the *learning zone* or a higher one, you have to be the exact opposite of a *closed-minded* person: **You need to have real humbleness, to acknowledge mistakes, to know how to ask for forgiveness, to research, to listen with interest, to learn positive and negative lessons from everyone, to observe, to be patient, unpretentious, comprehensive, to reflect over the advice that other people offer and to keep on walking regardless of the attacks from closed-minded people.**"

We arrived at the parking lot of his company. I was extremely surprised and somewhat nervous when I discovered that it was the same company where my father worked.

From the glove compartment, Don Joel took out an old worn book and wrote on the inside cover the address of a support group for the relatives of alcoholics.

"Go to this place. The meetings are every night at eight o'clock. Oh, and if you can, read this book."

He got out of the car and so did I.

"You've just explained to me the **two** sicknesses that my father has," I said to him, "but don't leave me hanging... What's the treatment?"

"To free yourself internally, to stop giving in to the addicted person and to practice loving confrontations. Those are the ***three stepping stones to recovery***. By reading this book and going to the support group, you'll understand them."

Damn, Don Joel and his technical terms! I needed to know these concepts urgently but I couldn't take anymore of his time.

"All right," I agreed. No one had guaranteed that the solutions to my problems would be free of charge.

I thanked him with a firm handshake and left happily, as if my batteries had just been recharged.

The pleasure didn't last long.

Barely approaching my house, I saw at a distance, the whole gang gathered in front of my building. Some were inside my uncle's video store, browsing, while others were watching for me.

I turned around and ran in the opposite direction.

"There goes Zahid!" yelled one of them, chasing me after alerting the rest of the gang.

---

1. Dr. Spickard and Barbara R. Thompson. "*Dying for a drink*". Vida Editorial.

2. John Boit Morse. "*Don't tell me I'm not an alcoholic*". Hazelden Foundation.

3. Dr. Spickard and Barbara R. Thompson. "*Dying for a drink*". Vida Editorial.

4. Vermon Coleman. "*Addicts and Addictions*". Grijalbo Editorial.

5. Dr. Jep Hoster. "*10 Things parents should know about drug and alcohol abuse*". Centenario Editions.

7

Internal freedom

As the pilot began to descend towards a nearby airport in order to refuel, I stared through the small window at the darkness of the sky. It hadn't been a quiet flight. More than once I had to pause in my story in order to seize the armrests and wait for the turbulence to subside.

I watched Lisbeth while she meditated and resisted the urge to kiss her. I loved her so much! We were two souls that had been unfairly hurt and in our search for help, our paths had crossed to complement each other and grow together.

"If my father had not been an alcoholic," I whispered, "and Don Joel had not suggested that I attend the support group, perhaps I wouldn't have ever met you."

She nodded with tenderness.

"In the long run, all wrong carries in itself a greater good."

She leaned on my shoulder and asked me to continue the story. So I did.[1]

Perhaps the gang had doubts about my guilt but, by running like crazy, I gave myself away immediately. Why didn't I confront them pretending not to know anything about the robbery at the warehouse? Why didn't I have the character to play the role of innocent? It was useless to try and amend what was already done.

I ran as fast as I could, knowing what I was escaping. They didn't forgive traitors. Even if I returned the money, no one could save me from a gang "bang", however, I couldn't even begin to imagine what would happen when they discovered I couldn't return it.

I crossed the main street at full speed and almost caused a car accident.

---

1. Note.- What I'm writing now is a narration as close as possible to the actual conversation that we held on the plane. I've calmly reconstructed it, adding only some support material from reliable sources.

I could feel them right behind me. I ran through the backyard of a house and while jumping their fence I fell on the sidewalk twisting my ankle, but at least I had made it safely to another street.

A bus was at the crossing and had just picked up passengers. Limping, I got to it as it was about to leave, I knocked on the door and the driver stopped to let me in. My pursuers were on the verge of catching up to me. They gathered one by one after the exhausting chase, to see how I had gotten away on the bus.

Although I was safe for the moment, they and I knew that we would meet again very soon.

I sat at the back of the bus fidgeting nervously with the book that Don Joel had lent me. It was an old mistreated book without a jacket.

I examined it as I leafed through it. It was called ***"Full of Internal Energy". The subtitle was a long phrase that read: "How to release yourself from your mental chains, based on the assertive systematical therapy elaborated by Dr. Manuel J. Smith."***

I tried to read it over and over again, but my mind just couldn't concentrate on the words. The gang was certainly a problem I would have to face sooner or later. Supposing that I managed to hide from them for a few days, eventually my vacation would end and then I would have to see them again at school. Crap! I had to do something. I couldn't just keep on running away.

I closed my eyes and tried to calm down. I'd find a solution. For the moment, I had to be careful.

My fear not only had me trapped in the *emotional zone*, but possibly had consumed all of the *energy from my self-esteem*.

I made a combination in my mind of the title and subtitle forming a phrase that seemed vitally important to me at the moment: "*Fill yourself with internal energy by liberating yourself from your mental chains...*"

I opened the book again, leafing through it and read a paragraph at random:

No one who lives with the mind shackled like a prisoner will ever be happy. The first step to achieve internal freedom is detaching yourself from the myths and lies that make you vulnerable enough to be manipulated.

I recalled that Don Joel had mentioned that this was the first stepping stone to recovery. Returning to the first chapter, I began reading with a renewed interest:

Liberate yourself from believing you are the protector of humanity. You have the right to reject the blame of others.

Helping, cooperating and giving, are the true attitudes of serving whose greatness comes from the voluntary generosity of the soul. These qualities lose their greatness when they're forced, pressured or manipulated by others.

It is time to start maturing. You have the right **to say no** *when another person tries to force you to pay for their blame.*

"Lend me money, do this for me, sacrifice yourself, give me, look after me, don't let me suffer, give me what you have..." Look out! These are phrases that are used to make you feel responsible for something that you're not. Millions of persons suffer dreadfully because they believe that they are responsible for the downfall of a loved one. Many parents who have problematic children live with a thorn nailed in their hearts feeling that they are to blame. The truth is that our attitudes can help others change the course of their lives, but in very few occasions are we responsible for their wrong doings. Each person can straighten the road of their own life if they want to and you're not responsible if they don't.

Free yourself from the pressure of suffering for others. Your children are not you. Their life is not yours. They're independent souls that have their own growth process, and that entails facing certain challenges and the pain of certain failures, whether you like it or not. Stop tearing your heart apart to overprotect them and simply help them to understand that you love them but that you don't have to suffer for their errors, because they are responsible for each of the consequences of their acts. In the long run they'll survive just fine.

You need to understand that you aren't the protector of humanity, that experiencing suffering is a way of improving our personal growth and that there's nothing bad about pain because it makes us better people. This is essential in order to be released from the first shackle.

Always remember: You have the right to reject the blame of others. Above all, if they are forcing you, because then you aren't doing it in the spirit of ***serving*** *or as a* ***mission,*** *but you're being controlled and no one can manipulate a mature person.*

I looked up from the book, confused by my mixed feelings. These were concepts that penetrated my understanding like explosive missiles and were tearing apart all my previous ideas.

My fear of the gang began to disappear and in its place, a tremendous realization of my ignorance invaded me. I was leaving the *emotional zone* and as I rose to the *learning zone*, I was finally able to comprehend that my salvation depended on this. I couldn't afford to ignore these techniques that others had used to escape the quicksand I was sinking into. I closed the book and contemplated its message. I'd read it again from beginning to end. I would memorize and apply it. As I opened it, I read the address that Don Joel had written on the inside cover. Glancing at the street I recognized where I was, not far from the place where the support group met.

It was very early to go there, but it didn't matter. I could read while I waited. I got off the bus and walked directly to the place.

I was surprised when I discovered an elegant conference hall. I admitted to the person in charge that it was my first time to sit in on a meeting and that my case was urgent. He informed me that the assembly room was shared by two different groups. The first gathered at five in the evening, but warned me that it was exclusively for women.

"Yours starts at eight o'clock at night." He looked at the clock and let out a whistle. "It's only going on one o'clock."

"I don't have anywhere to go." I told him. "Is there some place where I could sit and read while I wait? Please."

The man made an unpleasant scowl but allowed me to enter a small room which served as a lobby.

During the following four hours I read the whole book. Its ideas were completely opposite to my own and I was so astounded that I forgot about my exhaustion and hunger. I had truly found a stepping stone for my salvation.

At about four thirty the first woman that attended the support group arrived. She was surprised to see a man in the lobby, but I didn't pay any attention. To her amazement, I asked if she could lend me a marker to highlight the more important parts of the book.

She gave me one mechanically and I began underlining immediately:

Free yourself from the obligation of being perfect.
You have the right to make mistakes and to pay for them.

If you make a mistake, accept it, don't defend yourself, don't look for justifications. Engrave this in your mind: ***you have the right to make mistakes.*** *As many as you need in order to learn the lessons of life.*

Just as it's good that others learn from their failures without your being obligated to rescue them, also understand and accept that your own blunders make you a better person. Did you do something wrong yesterday? That's all right. It's part of your walking through life. Understand this: In the future you will continue making mistakes but don't feel discouraged or be afraid to take new risks. Continue moving, deciding, acting, even if you make an error.

Of course, it's not enough to know that our failures serve a purpose. You need to understand also that ***these mistakes produce pain*** *and that you have to face the consequences responsibly. For example: You're walking down the street, absent-mindedly, and you stumble into a pole.* ***You have the right*** *to hit your head against all the poles in the city until you learn to dodge them but, please, don't get upset with the pole or with yourself, don't kick it or vent your frustration on it. The blow hurts but it's the* ***price*** *you pay for your mistake. Expect to pay for it gracefully and* ***learn the lesson.*** *Each mistake has its price and you have to pay it willingly. If it's money, with money, if it's pain (physical or emotional), with pain, if it's work, with work.*

Perhaps your friend laughs and calls you clumsy, foolish or stupid.

Laugh with him, but don't believe the labels he's giving you because ***you aren't****, you simply made a mistake. To say to people* ***"you are,"*** *accompanied by humiliating adjectives, is disrespectful rudeness. Don't let some manipulator hang permanent names on you and if they have, take them off once and for all. You* ***ARE NOT*** *stupid, ugly, insecure, shy, clumsy, slow, bad in mathematics, bad in sports nor bad for all the things that others have made you believe. You are, in reality, a great human being, a child of God, a potential success. When you make a mistake and someone says to you "****you are...****", don't take him seriously. You have the right to make mistakes because your blunders will hurt only you and no one else, and you'll be responsible for their consequences.*

I recalled the "you are's" of my mother (stupid, ungrateful and irresponsible) and how bad they had made me feel. Maybe she was right in scolding me for arriving home late, but I WAS NOT any of the things that she had called me. In any event, I made a mistake and the police, Don Joel and even my own father made me pay an expensive price for it. It was a beautiful way of looking at life and of removing the heavy chains of insecurity.

I continued highlighting:

Free yourself from being rigid.
You have the right to change your opinion.

Beginning in our tender childhood years, we've been taught that once we've voiced our preferences, we cannot change our minds.

Being terrified to change your course of action for fear that someone will become annoyed, is an irresponsible and childish reaction. Eliminate that habit, erase it from your mind. Being ***rigid*** *is a debilitating chain that easily allows you to become a puppet of others, since it forces you to remain tied to your past decisions (which perhaps at the time were correct but now aren't applicable anymore). People and circumstances change; what you considered appropriate before might not be now because you are seeing things in a new light.* ***You have the right to change your opinion.***

As you can imagine, one must realize there's also a price for exercis-

ing this right. Frequently, when you change your opinion it can mean financial setbacks, starting over, facing upsetting situations, etcetera. However, when you balance what you lost against what you gain in order to get going, then you really have your feet on the ground and know what is best for you. Don't feel that your hands are tied only because you endorsed something. That's nonsense which only makes you an easy victim of manipulators. ***You have the right to change your opinion.*** *If you buy something and don't like it, return it; if you announce that you're starting a certain business, but later on change your mind because something different will benefit you more, go back to square one. Doing so isn't a sign of immaturity but of intelligence. Of course only a few will understand, the rest will say you're inconsistent and will make you feel guilty for changing your mind, however, if they manage to intimidate you and you give in, the consequences will eventually harm you in the future. Stop yourself... Thousands of people without clear values or morals, try very hard to defend their position even though they know it's wrong. Millions of human beings live putting up with terrible situations when deep inside they'd like to change and free themselves from these pressures that are part of their past. Those who can't rise above their need for approval (zone) tend to panic worrying about what others think and this forces them to do things they really don't want to do. Simply put,* ***only the courageous have the guts to escape****. If in the heat of the moment you're challenged to a fist fight and swear you'll do something irrational, wake up and rethink what you really want. Don't let anyone or anything force you to make wrong choices you'll regret later...* ***You have the right to change your opinion.***

What kind of philosophy was this? It scared me and overpowered me. How could it be that I had lived all my life based on lies? These concepts were dangerous, because if a person without a conscience adopted them, he could forget about his responsibilities, leave his children, wife, work and country only because he exerted his right to change his opinion. However, it also stated very clearly that to exercise this right you had to pay a price.

(*Frequently, when you change your opinion it can mean financial setbacks, starting over, facing upsetting situations, etcetera; but when you balance what you lost against what you gain in order to get going, then you really have your feet on the ground and know what is best for you.)*

Some months back, Alma, my mother and I had promised dad that we would stand by him and help him unconditionally, but by fulfilling that promise we were all becoming deeply hurt. Furthermore, by silently allowing his mistakes to continue without letting him pay for them, resulted in his sinking increasingly deeper into the quicksand of irresponsibility. The whole family **had the right to reject carrying the burden of my father's behavior** and now, seeing things under a new light, mother, Alma and I should **openly take back** our promise to tolerate him.

I looked around.

The room was filling up with women. I looked down and hurriedly underlined one more idea before I was asked to return the marker.

Free yourself from the obligation of knowing it all. You have the right to say "I don't know," or "I don't understand."

Narrow-minded people try to make others feel bad by showing them how ignorant they are. They'll ask if you've read a certain book, if you know a certain character, or if you are aware of the latest news; always waiting for you to prove your shortcomings so they can pounce gleefully and throw it back in your face... Remember, you don't have any reason to pretend that you know something if you really don't. Rip off the shackles. ***You have the right to say "I don't know" or "I don't understand."*** *If they ask your opinion, don't worry, you can simply answer I DON'T KNOW. If someone demands something unreasonable from you, tell him you don't understand why he is asking and don't give in until he explains everything to your entire satisfaction. If someone is annoyed and you don't know the reason, ask him openly for an explanation because you* ***don't understand*** *his attitude.* ***The secret of wise men is to observe and learn to accept, over and over again, how to say "I don't know", while letting others explain.*** *If you don't know or understand something, say so. Instead of feeling insignificant, be proud every time* *you have the opportunity to say I DON'T KNOW, or I DON'T UNDERSTAND because, by admitting it, you might learn something new and then, each day will have more meaning for you.*

Free yourself from playing the role of "the victim or the accused." You have the right not to give explanations.

If you don't do exactly what others want, they'll corner you, forcing you to defend yourself.

However, anytime you decide to act maturely,[2]. you have the right to:

–Refuse to carry someone else's blame,

–Make mistakes and pay for them,

–Change your opinion,

–Say "I don't know," or "I don't understand."

People will invariably demand that you justify what you did or said. As soon as you answer, they'll attack you again with another ***"why?"****. To each one of your responses, the manipulator will be ready to make you feel foolish and you'll become the accused. Listen, free yourself from being victimized.* ***You have the right not to give any explanations.***

If a manipulator annoys you or tries to make you accept his conditions, don't get angry; calmly demonstrate your disapproval and persevere without explaining anything more. When facing a narrow-minded person that insists on manipulating you, you'll need to be tenacious but never lose control; state clearly and repeat what you believe or want. Don't argue or try to convince him with excuses, but only say what you feel. Insist, even if your words don't answer what he asks, continue as if you had swallowed a cassette player that repeats the same thing over and over again. ***Perseverance without anger*** *totally disarms the narrow-minded, forcing them to give up although unwillingly. The key to the formula is* ***persistence with serenity****. Don't forget it. Don't listen to the threats of the manipulator. If he says* ***no*** *ONCE, you'll say yes TWICE, if he insists SIX times, you'll do it SEVEN, if he has ELEVEN phrases to*

---

[2]. Manuel J. Smith. *"When I say no, I feel guilty"*, Grijalbo Editorial.

try and make you fall, you'll have TWELVE to maintain yourself firm. As simple as that, without screaming, without getting upset, repeating again and again your point of view you'll avoid falling into the trap of answering his questions or giving explanations and excuses.

The sound of the microphone in the hall distracted me. The women had begun their meeting. When I looked up there was a very beautiful young woman standing and observing me. It wasn't the one who had lent me the marker because she had probably seen me concentrating so hard that she preferred not to disturb me. No. Apparently the woman who watched me had arrived late and stopped to study me before entering the room.

I stood up and sat down again. I closed the book, then opened it and stammered that I was waiting for the Alanon meeting.

"I won't disturb you. I'll stay right here. I'm only reading."

The young woman smiled and turned to leave me alone. Before she went into the room I asked her to wait a minute, I got up again and approached her asking in a confidential tone:

"Tell me something. Just out of curiosity. What's your name and what sort of group is this?"

The woman moved back with evident distrust on her face. Of my two questions, what did one have to do with the other? She watched me cautiously and slowly answered:

"My name is Lisbeth and this is a support group for victims of rape."

Saying that, she closed the door.

8

Rape

Lisbeth was lost in her memories.

The plane had taken off again after refueling and we found ourselves flying through clear, quiet skies. For a few moments we had both forgotten that we were making a trip.

"When I saw you that afternoon," she confessed, speaking very slowly, "concentrating so hard on your book to the extent that you didn't hear the lady who asked you for her pen or the leader who asked you to leave, I concluded that you seemed rather strange. I was one of the guest speakers that night and a little nervous, but that didn't keep me from noticing the peculiar fact that a young man would be reading by the door of a support group for women."

"And I couldn't continue reading after you entered the hall so I decided to spy on the meeting. I couldn't believe that a woman like you needed to be there." I hugged her. "Now tell me how you ended up at that place. What happened with Martin after they found him drugged?"

She took a deep breath and glanced at her watch.

"We'll be arriving soon. I won't have enough time to tell you everything."

"It doesn't matter. Start now."

"Zahid. We could jump to the facts without getting into the details."

"That was not the deal."

"I know, but," she stopped, "it will make me very uncomfortable to have to remember. Besides, you may feel hurt when you hear it all."

I looked at her, a little bit annoyed.

"All right," she agreed, "but don't say that I didn't warn you."

I told you that my dad took me to see Martin, while he was drugged in a dark slum and when we got back home I confessed my pregnancy causing my world to collapse as I watched how my family, who I depended on the most, reject me.

I was laying on the floor when the telephone rang. It was Martin's father who insisted on asking me if I knew what drugs his son was using.

After Martin's father gave me the directions to the hospital, I left the receiver on the table and started walking toward the street. Everything around me was a haze, as if the furniture and my family were surrounded by a fog that kept me from seeing them clearly.

"Where're you going?" asked Dad.

"What do you care?" I answered.

"It's eleven o'clock at night. I can't let you go out alone at this hour."

"You can't let me?" I began to laugh like a madwoman, "and with what right? You've already washed your hands of your responsibility and resigned your authority over me."

Dad remained motionless and without the strength to articulate even a single word after my sudden retaliation.

Striding rapidly, I escaped into the street, desperately trying to confuse the malicious ghost that had declared me his. I felt naive, stupid, seduced.

I turned a corner and faced a long solitary street. Cars went by at intervals of five to ten minutes. One of them stopped ahead of me and waited patiently for me to walk by; the young "jocks" assured me that they hadn't seen a more beautiful woman that night and asked me if I needed to go somewhere. I refused to answer and continued walking; they followed me trying to convince me. I ignored them and after a while, they took off, squeaking their tires and making some obscene gestures through the windows.

I asked myself over and over again what had I seen in Martin? Why had I given in to him?

When I told him that I was pregnant, he promised to do the right thing, but still, if he stopped using drugs forever, would I really want to take the risk of marrying him? In a chauvinist society, who had more opportunities of starting her life over? A divorcee with a son or an unwed mother? The options were very limited.

"It's better to be alone than with the wrong person," I said to myself, "although, really, *it's much better to be with the right person than alone.* If he recovers and makes a real effort," I concluded, "maybe I'd risk marrying him and try and form a family that would at least make me feel better instead of everyone feeling sorry for me and continuing to treat me like a foolish idiot who made a mistake. Besides, even if my marriage failed, I'd still feel better for having tried."

My anguish tormented me again and I wiped away my tears furiously. I had to lift my head up high and without shame in order to get ahead with my child, one way or another. I couldn't understand why this had happened to me? Realizing that I couldn't control myself, I jogged for a while until my strength was spent and stopped. I bent over and burst out crying uncontrollably.

I suddenly felt the presence of a car behind me. The sound of the motor scarcely a few meters away, made me realize that someone was watching me. The car had the lights off. I didn't move. I had the feeling that it was the same young studs. What more could happen to me? I was exhausted, unable to defend myself. I stayed down for a few more minutes, waiting without turning. As time went by and no one approached, my survival instincts made me stand up and start walking with my head down. Suddenly, my body bumped into the body of a man that was standing right in front of me. I was terrified. I looked up. It was my father.We stared at each other for a few seconds.

There wasn't any reproach left in his eyes, only sorrow and worry.

There wasn't any more anger in mine either, only a great remorse.

Then I embraced him and he embraced me. In tears, I said to him:

"Please forgive me, please... I failed you. I failed you all. You can't imagine how I feel. Forgive me..."

He couldn't say a word. We remained in each other's arms and, while we were like this, I finally understood how terrible it must be for a father to see his daughter deceived, going in the wrong direction, having resigned her dreams, and all because of a wrong sexual decision.

"I love you, Lisbeth." he finally said, hesitating. "The shock was very hard for me to endure because I never imagined something like this could ever happen to you, but please, I didn't mean to hurt you."

His "I love you" seemed very different from the one that he had said hours before...

The tears didn't let me answer him, or let him say anything else. Father and daughter, embraced in the darkness of a solitary street, attempting to comfort each other from something that hurt them both to the depths of their souls, and that would transform their lives forever.

He led me to the car and opened the passenger door, asking:

"Do you want to go to the hospital?"

I nodded.

He drove without saying a word. I put my head on his lap like a little girl, the girl that he once had taught how to swim and to play tennis, the girl that had always been his pride and joy. He caressed my head telling me that nothing had changed between us.

Arriving at the hospital, we found Martin's parents immediately.

"How is he?" I asked.

"In serious condition. Excuse me for having called your house, but the doctors wanted, or I should say, *needed* to know about the drugs or combination of substances that he's taken."

At the moment, I didn't realize that his father's question really offended me since they assumed I was doing drugs with their son.

With a hopeful look, we saw a physician arrive. The anxious parents interrogated him and the doctor informed us that Martin was in very serious condition due to the fact that the tests indicated he had taken an overdose of crack combined with alcohol.

"Doctor," questioned my father, immediately, "I know that this is not the right time or place, but please tell me something. Is there any risk that he has *AIDS*?"

"No. You don't have to worry about that. The type of drug that he consumed is not injected, and that exempts him from the greater percentage of risk."

Martin's father followed the doctor but we stayed with his pathetic looking mother. She watched us with distrust. Perhaps she was annoyed by my Dad's question or simply she had found the right moment to pour out the poison stored up in her bitter and possessive mother's soul.

"Things have always gone wrong for my poor son," she said. "The problems in his romantic relationships have definitely affected him. Since he separated from his wife, he hasn't been the same. Women seem to have damaged him a lot."

For a moment I thought that she was talking about someone else. It was my father who reacted more rapidly.

"What are you saying? Martin was married before?"

My boyfriend's mother seemed upset by making us believe that she regretted having said "too much", but her words were perfectly calculated.

"Yes," she said, with a fake shyness. "He was eighteen and the woman twenty-four. She was skillful and trapped him by getting pregnant.They got married, but not in a church. They only lasted eighteen months together. Didn't you know?"

I shook my head. All I knew about Martin was that he worked in a wine company as a sales executive, he had a beautiful car, an elegant presence, and he claimed to be an engineer who was prepared to formalize his relationship with me.

"Is Martin an engineer?" I heard myself asking.

"No. He always wanted to be one, but since he got married so young, he had to leave his studies and started working in order to support his family. He dropped out in his last year of high school. Things didn't go well for him. His wife manipulated him."

"And does he work in a wine company?"

"He did, but he resigned. They exploited him. His boss was a tyrant. Now he helps my husband a little. He's a good boy, but he's still recovering, emotionally."

A *good boy*? Then certainly I was, for the myopic overprotective mother, another harpy attempting to trap her innocent baby. I was boiling mad. Whatever I'd say, she would use against me.

"Let's go, Dad."

My father took me by the arm and we both turned around without saying good-bye.

He didn't say anything on the way home. He didn't ask me again how I had let myself be deceived. He was as outraged as I was.

A week and a half later, I got a telephone call from Martin. I didn't want to talk to him. Dad had forbidden me from speaking to him and I obeyed. However, since he had insisted over and over again, after a few days I got to thinking that, at least, I should give him the opportunity to explain things. He was the father of my child. Only he could assure me that his mother hadn't made up all of what she said in order to keep me from him, forcing me to face my pregnancy alone. I needed to know if he had lied.

We arranged a secret meeting. I told him that I'd be waiting to be picked up at the corner, since I needed to hear his side of the story. Only my mother knew about the secret rendezvous. When he arrived, I wasn't impressed anymore by his beautiful car or elegant appearance.

"This is your Dad's car, right?"

"Who told you that?"

"Stop pretending, okay?"

"Where do you want me to take you?"

"To a quiet place so we can talk clearly."

He drove carefully. I observed his profile, unable to believe that someone so good-looking could be so deceitful.

"Have you quit doing drugs?"

"I never did," he answered without looking at me, "that night I was the victim of a prank. My friends forced me to do drugs and I passed out."

I didn't believe him, but why argue. Distracted and lost in my thoughts, I didn't realize that we were driving into a motel until the car stopped and I looked up.

"And this? Where have you brought me?"

"It's a quiet place. Here we can talk calmly and in private."

"Wait a minute. If you think that you have the right, you are very wrong. First let's lay the cards on the table and talk about conditions and responsibilities."

"Don't be ridiculous. You and I are like husband and wife."

"What did you say?" I screamed hysterically. "Get me out of here immediately!"

Shocked by my crazed fury, he started the car and left the motel. He stepped on the gas pedal and drove in the fast lane. His facial features were transformed into a hard bittered grimace. He drove so fast that for a moment I imagined that he wanted to kill us both.

"Can you slow down?"

"So, I don't have *any* rights?"

I grasped on to the seat for dear life and began to feel beads of sweat run down my forehead. We left the city and found ourselves on a solitary highway.

"Where are we going? Take me back to my house!"

The road was in such bad shape it seemed to be under construction. We finally got to a spot surrounded by trees and he stopped the car.

At some distance there was a small, abandoned log cabin.

"Very well," he said, turning toward me with bloodshot eyes, "is this place all right to talk about *conditions and responsibilities?*"

I glanced around. It was getting dark and there was no way of escaping or calling for help.

"Yes." I tried to appear calm. "Now tell me about your past and don't you dare lie to me. Is it true that you got married when you were eighteen and that you have a child with another woman?"

"She manipulated me. I was a kid. I didn't do it for love. Now I can try to start my life all over again, don't you think? With you it's different. I want to have a real home."

He came close to me and hugged me, but I tensed up.

"Stop." I pushed him back. "I want to talk."

He mocked me by saying, "about *conditions and responsibilities?*"

He embraced me again and began to kiss my face intensely. For a moment I remained still without knowing what to do. His gestures and movements seemed very sweet, however, the difference now was his kisses disgusted me.

Unexpectedly, he lowered his hand to fondle my breast. I felt angry and pushed his hand while I moved back.

"That's enough. Not now!"

"Come here." He pulled me again, imprisoning me, and this time his tone sounded perversely angry. "You're mine, don't you understand? Don't you realize that no one else will want you now? These are the cards on the table: You belong to me! There's nothing more to say."

"Leave me alone..."

He hugged me with such force that I began to feel asphyxiated.

"I want you, I need you." He tried to be sensuous, licking my neck and ear with his filthy tongue.

I felt helpless and defeated.

"Don't tell me you don't like to make love. Last time you cooperated more. What's wrong with you? Enjoy it!"

"I can't breathe."

He released me and began to unbutton my blouse. He seemed like a stranger to me.

"Please," I stopped him.

Sarcastically, he repeated, "pl..ea..se..." and he immobilized me again with his embrace.

What was happening? Was this violent seduction or subtle rape?

Without permitting me much movement, he finished unbuttoning my blouse and started to undo my bra. I was terrified. When I resisted, he seemed dreadfully harsh and squeezed my breasts with so much force that they hurt, but when I remained still, he seemed amiable and even affectionate.

"I don't like this place to make love," I said to him, attempting to make him stop and gain time. "You were right, why don't we go to the hotel?"

He stopped and seemed to agree. While he started the car, I hurried to fix my clothes.

When everything indicated that we would leave, he turned the key and stopped the car.

"Are you trying to be smart with me?"

"No, honey."

I put my hand on his shoulder, but he noticed that I was nervous, and grasped me.

"You'll do whatever I say and wherever I say it. So unbutton that blouse again."

At that moment, two young men came out of the deteriorated cabin. They waved at Martin and approached us.

As they walked towards the car, I noticed that they had a hard time keeping their balance.

"I thought that there was no one here," said my abductor as if he was talking to one of his family members.

"Here we are," one of them answered, "just us..."

"Do you have any powder?"

It was then when I realized that I was trapped.

I opened the door of the car and attempted to run, but my movement was so rapid and unexpected that I fell to the ground next to the car. Martin quickly stretched across the seat and grabbed me by my wrist. The strangers hurried to help their friend.

"Is the baby trying to escape?"

"She's a slut..."

Both of them began jumping with excitement like children allowed to join a game just in the nick of time. One of them approached me and put his shoe on my forearm so I couldn't get up while Martin finished getting out of the car and unzipping his fly. His gesture was cruel and decisive. He glared at me in a crude way, something I had never seen him do before. He finished pulling out his genitals and sat on my stomach, immobilizing me.

The two druggies were laughing.

"Eat me."

"Let me go, you pig." I spit and turned my head to the side.

He crushed my arms with his knees and once his hands were free, he straightened my head to force me to look at him.

"Please," I begged him. "You're going to hurt the baby."

"Shut up, bitch!" He raised my head and slapped me hard. "You're spoiling it all."

I watched him, feeling terrified. Why was he beating me? I still didn't understand that an irrational demonic desire to possess me, to dominate me, had overtaken him. He smiled with disdain and kept slamming the back of my neck against the ground over and over again. I knew that my life was in danger.

Many times I'd heard that in a rape it's better not to resist, since it's only the sexual act, but in reality it's **not** a sexual act, it's a filthy and degrading assault. Weeks later, at the support group, I listened to the testimony of a woman who was raped with a broken bottle. She had to have twenty stitches and had been on the verge of death.

"If you can defend yourself," he said to me, "do it now!"

When I was little I studied martial arts, but that is a complex discipline that takes years to master, more than karate; a woman must develop her self-esteem to be brave and agile enough to scream, run, stick her nails in his throat, punch his nose, stick her fingers in his eyes, beat his testicles and exert other acts of aggression that require more skill and decision than force. At that instant, my sixth sense made me realize he would kill me if I resisted, however, my self-dignity revolted against being humiliated like that.

The idea of biting him crossed my mind, but I hesitated and he noticed.

"Don't you dare."

He slapped me four times with an open hand.

My face seemed to be on fire.

He suddenly stood up, giving me a slight chance to try and run away, but one of his friends grabbed me by the hair.

"Come here."

Between the three of them, pulling and ripping, they took my clothes off one by one until they left me totally naked. Crazed with laughter, they threw me into the arms of one and then another.

Martin pulled his pants down and made me turn around, forcing me to bend forward. It was very painful. I screamed, I wept, but there was no one near.

"We'll protect the baby like this."

I fell into some sort of trance, as if my soul had abandoned my body for some moments to separate me from what was happening.

When people talk about sexual abuse we tend to think: "that will never happen to me," but conservatively speaking, it's known that it happens to thirty percent of all women. Any woman can be a victim of rape. In the same way, any man can commit rape, but the majority decide not to. Women, on the other hand, don't have a choice. Furthermore, there are disturbing statistics that are rarely mentioned. According to the victims in a survey for women's safety, three fourths of all sexual abuses are committed by acquaintances well known to the victim, such as: boyfriends, neighbors, classmates, colleagues at work, bosses and relatives. There's a false belief that all rapists are mentally unbalanced monsters that go out at night, masked and armed, and even though there are some of that kind, they're the minority. Regularly, the violator who forces himself sexually, plans it, fantasizes about the idea before carrying it out and too frequently the victim lives very close to him, sometimes in the same house or neighborhood.[1]

I don't remember what they made me do after that, but what I do remember I'd rather not say. Even now it's difficult for me to believe all that happened and express it in words. For more than an hour, the three of them did all sorts of disgusting things to me. Yet, the most absurd thing was that when they were done, they forced me to get dressed and get in the car as if nothing had happened. The friends sat in the back seat and Martin drove back to the city.

"All women really enjoy a little bit of force," he theorized, "they entice and provoke us until they get what they want, and then, I'm sure they can't help but like it too."

What I heard was incredible. Now I know this idea is generally accepted. Many jokes, stories and even movies demonstrate the grotesque scene of a young woman who wants to be raped and when she is, begs for more. There's nothing as absurdly damaging and prejudicial to our society than to believe and make stupid jokes of that kind. It's easy to laugh about what isn't understood. It's true, a woman can enjoy the sexual act the same as a man; for example, we can compare this to a father enjoying the company of his son while teaching him how to swim holding his breath under water, however,

---

[1] Jane Dowdeswell. "*Women on Rape*". Grijalbo Editorial.

I'd dare to ask if that same man would enjoy being forced to hold his breath with his head inside a toilet full of shit. A moment of affection cannot be compared to a humiliating and perverse criminal offense.

On the way back, one of Martin's friends said that the next time they would invite me to watch one of their movies so that I would relax more and then they wouldn't have to hurt me. Today I know that pornography encourages rapes. Scenes in which a woman is sexually violated with brutal force, pervert the normal way of thinking about sex for many men and, although the majority would never dare initiate anything criminal, many others will, as they're strongly motivated by the fantasies of sexual deviation which they become familiar with, through porno films.

When we arrived at my house, I opened the gate and hurried into the yard, but just before getting to the front door, I stopped in my tracks, devastated, I felt like my heart had burst into a million pieces.

Through the living room window, I could see my father waiting for me.

9

Sexual differences

I took off my safety belt and tried to stand up inside the plane, but the ceiling was so low that I could only manage to take a step by crouching down. I was furious and deeply affected. Never had I felt so much anger, not in my entire life.

"What happened to that bastard?" I asked my wife, "is he dead? Because if he's alive, he better watch out."

"You see? I told you it would be better not to go into all of this."

I collapsed on the seat and closed my eyes recalling how the leader of our gang raped a woman, precisely after we had become aroused at a topless bar. It was virtually impossible to go out with the girls that danced on tables exhibiting their nude bodies. However, once we left the guarded club, there were many defenseless females at our disposal, as our leader demonstrated. My own personal torment was the worst punishment knowing that although I didn't participate, neither did I prevent a rape; and realizing I had witnessed it made me grasp the fact that the woman could have been my wife...

"Please finish."

I wanted to run to my father, to cry out to him, but I didn't move. Did it make sense to complain of having been raped after disobeying his specific orders, meeting Martin with whom I had been sexually active? Who would believe me? And in any event, who would care? If I forgot about the two drug addicts and the fact that it was a gang rape, my position was similar to that of a married woman accusing her husband of sexual abuse. In today's society it's accepted that if you consent once, you're obligated to always comply.

I heard Martin's car leave. I was morally crushed. I felt that I had no strength left to go on. I felt like a useless doll that had lost its batteries forever.

After a while my mother came out. She asked me what happened, but I told her nothing, I simply didn't move or react. She detected something was wrong and tried to guess.

"What you have to realize," she said, walking up to me, "is that your boyfriend simply doesn't want you. We're just going to have to accept the idea."

I nodded and she put her arm around my back.

"It's not that bad. If he doesn't want to marry you, perhaps it's for the best." She led me to the house holding my arm. "I know you must be very disappointed, but don't worry. It'll be all right. Tell me, were you clear with him? Did you make him see his obligations and responsibilities? What did he say? My God! You really look awful! Come on now, don't be so upset..."

I didn't want to say a single word. I felt like a zombie who had come back from the dead. Walking with mechanical steps, I went slowly to my room. My mom followed me, but stopped in the hallway when she saw that I wasn't going to say a word. I closed the door in her face, locking it and collapsed on the floor.

I spent the night there, still feeling trapped as if the weight of a mountain was pressing down on me. I felt nauseous, repugnant; submerged in sewage, without any energy to get up. In my own eyes, I was nothing more than a filthy corpse, the worst garbage that was surely putrefying faster than I could ever imagine. Since I knew the principal violator so well, I felt guilty that I had provoked the rape. Nothing is more paralyzing than being convinced that you participated and were responsible for something like that. The *energy from your self-esteem* goes drastically down the drain.

At eight o'clock in the morning, mom knocked on my door.

I woke up and managed to drag myself very slowly to the bathroom. I had to force myself to put one foot in front of the other, as if

I were handicapped and just learning to walk. I turned on the shower and, without adjusting the temperature, entered fully clothed under the icy cold water, activating every cell in my body and turning my depression into overwhelming rage. I removed my clothes and searched under the sink for cleaning supplies, finding disinfectant, pumice and a brillo pad, I took them back into the shower and began scrubbing my body very hard. I ended up with deep abrasions in some areas. I wanted to make sure that no one would smell my stench. I put on a turtleneck sweater so that the scratches weren't visible, but I didn't put on any make-up or comb my hair.

I went to school in search of my psychology teacher and barged into her classroom without permission.

"I'm going to kill myself," I declared. When she turned to look at me, my voice became shaky.

I had interrupted the class.

"Hello, Lisbeth. Is there a problem?"

"I'm going to end my life right now."

"What are you saying?" the alarmed teacher approached me, realizing I wasn't kidding.

The students silently observed. I was frozen to the spot.

"Please sit down," she invited me. "We'll talk as soon as the class is over."

I shook my head and marched out of the room.

"Stop!!" she ordered, following behind me, but I didn't obey.

When she caught up to me, she forced me to turn around and face her.

"What's going on with you?"

"I hate everyone!! I'm afraid to walk down the street, I feel like garbage walking around garbage. I look at men and think they're all animals. I've lost the desire to live. And the baby inside of me... A few days ago I felt comforted by him, but now I wish I could destroy him."

The psychologist froze, staring at me. Some time later, she confessed to me how shocked she was by the seriousness of my problem.

"Let's go to my office."

"If a person you trust abuses you," I screamed, ignoring her invitation, "you can't trust anyone anymore! Do you understand me?"

Then, just as if a dam had burst, my feelings came gushing out. Those were hard yet important moments for me. My teacher listened very attentively to me, I screamed, wept and cursed in the middle of the school courtyard without caring about the curious looks from the other students. My purging was taking on a different tone after a few minutes, and I realized I needed more privacy.

She led me to her office. After pouring out my soul I felt better, like a person in agony who had just vomited most of the poison that was killing her. I asked to use her restroom and when I saw myself in the mirror I felt ashamed of my own reflection. Quickly I fixed my hair and while straightening my sweater, I noticed the red welts on my arms; covering them I said to myself, "This is going to change!"

I came out with a hard look on my face and said decidedly:

"The fact that men are given public, political, financial and entrepreneurial jobs, and that women are left with the children and the household chores, signifies for many men, that they have the right to dominate us and trample our wills, but what is really pathetic is that, sadly enough, many women believe that they don't have the right to defend themselves. But I'm not going to stand still with my arms crossed. I will press charges, no matter what happens, I'll see this thing through to the end. I want to see them pay dearly for what they did to me."

She nodded slowly and suggested:

"But don't do it alone."

"Why not? I've always been alone."

"But you have parents and sisters."

For a moment, I didn't know what to say.

"I'd prefer not to get them involved."

"Why? **The measure of a loving family is how they stay together and support each other, in the good times and bad...**"

"Perhaps... but I'm not sure that I can share *this* with them..."

I stood up. My teacher remained quiet. Finally she asked:

"Would you let me go with you?"

I smiled.

"Thanks, I'd really appreciate that."

We spent nearly the whole day at the police station. I had to give detailed statements and go through a special medical examination. Contrary to what I had imagined, the doctor was very kind and gentle. While I was being examined, I thought to myself how lucky I had been since not all victims of rape are as fortunate as I was.

I informed them of all the pertinent evidence necessary to arrest Martin. My teacher and I went with an inspector to the place where I was raped and all the proof found there was recorded. The tire marks were still there as well as a couple of buttons from my blouse. They checked the cabin but didn't find anything. Finally, the experts told me that as soon as the suspects were detained, I would have to identify them. They recommended that until then, I should hire an attorney.

"It's not obligatory," they explained, "but it will be very helpful at the hearing. The most difficult part is still to come. I don't know if we'll catch the other two, but at least Martin will argue that you did it voluntarily. This sort of trial is long and difficult for the woman. The majority withdraw the charges after having to put up with countless embarrassing set-backs."

"I will get legal help."

"There's a support group for women where you'll be able to find a specialist in this area."

He gave me a card with the information.

We left at about six o'clock in the evening, exhausted. My teacher invited me to eat a hamburger.

"I hate men," I repeated as soon as we sat down at the fast-food restaurant, "they're all bastards! Did you see how the policemen looked at us? I bet that they kept on asking me for more details because they're sick too, and not because of the investigation. They're all the same. There's no doubt about that."

The psychologist shook her head in disagreement, but delayed her answer. After all, we weren't in therapy, at the moment we were just two friends exchanging ideas.

Finally, my teacher started to explain: "As human beings we have the unconscious tendency of turning specific experiences into general laws. When we think like this, it's easy to stereo-type that this race is dirty, or that country is materialistic or those of another group are promiscuous, labeling one group as thieves or another as lazy. When it's all really a big lie. The mistakes of some *are not* the mistakes of all. It's true that there are some really depraved people, but the vast majority of men and women are decent."

I felt confused and argued, "I don't believe it. This world is a piece of crap. The news tells us this all the time."

"Why are you closing your mind, Lisbeth?"

"Because it's true!"

"You're wrong!" She leaned forward as if trying to teach me something very obvious. "The newspapers, television and movies sell *news*. They're devoted to seeking sensational events and making them public as if they were the only things happening. If a man commits a crime, it makes the front page, but if on that same day, millions of other men work hard to provide for their families, no one acknowledges this; if a woman kills her children, it will be a huge case, but if hundreds of dedicated mothers on the same night lose sleep caring for their sick children, the world will ignore it. I know what happened to you yesterday is very painful, but **that doesn't mean that *all* men are the same.** There are many with extraordinary qualities who live and believe in honesty and respect. **To condemn all men would be as illogical as wanting to terminate the entire animal kingdom only because you were bit by a dog.**"

"That makes sense," I said, almost crying, "but I feel so violated, so sexually demoralized, no one is going to love me now..."

"What you're saying is absurd! **What ruins life isn't an event, but your interpretation of it.** It's a matter of ideas. Don't limit your way of thinking. What can be normal for one culture, can be wrong for another. If you say 'it's the end,' it is. If, on the contrary you tell yourself, 'the real me is still intact, I refuse to swallow this poison and become bitter,' then nothing happened because you chose to become healed, you only suffered an accident like any other..."

I interrupted her, "Perhaps you're right, but I'm full of hatred..."

My teacher remained silent for a long while. She looked at her watch and said:

"It'll help you a lot to listen to the testimonies of other women who have lived through the same thing that you have. You should go to the support group today. If we hurry, we'll be able to get there on time."

We finished eating our hamburgers without saying anything more, then we got up and left. She took me to the meeting and said goodbye, excusing herself for not being able to stay.

The women at the meeting seemed so cheerful, so properly dressed and with such pleasant expressions on their faces that for a moment I thought they were actresses trained to give a normal everyday appearance masking the tragedy for those who had actually suffered. "This is a circus," I said to myself.

When they saw me enter, they invited me courteously to a designated place, since the meeting had already started.

There was a speaker, who was an expert in her field, lecturing at the front:

"Many of you probably have wondered at some point, why men and women don't look at sex in the same way? Why is it so difficult for us to see the real intentions of our friends and male companions?"

I glanced around me. The place was cozy and silent. There were about thirty women of all ages. The voice of the guest speaker grabbed my attention once again.

"The Law of Pareto states that the relationships between men and women can be explained in this way: **Men react 80% with sexuality and 20% romanticism, but women, on the other hand, are 80% romantic and 20% sexual.** That **doesn't** mean that men are sex feigns or that women are perfect angels, what it does mean is that our integral design as individuals is a mixture of our sexuality and our emotional need for love, producing a special combination. Men mix both behaviors and are easily excited contemplating the female body, therefore, overwhelmed with the desire to conquer and carnally aroused, they can easily become polygamous. On the other hand, women are much more conscious of their need to love, serve, keep house, be emotionally stable and maintain the peace. But these tendencies do not mean that one or the other will be ONLY like this. With his 20% of romanticism a man also knows how to be tender, spontaneous and can act like a gentleman or a poet, and the woman with her 20% of sexuality is sensuous, provocative, passionate and active in intimacy. However, this last point must be taken in perspective since it is not the dominant part. **Men and women make the great mistake of considering themselves equal to each other and, believing this, they base their relationships on this error.** Men believe that we can feel the same sexual desire in the same way that they can, and women believe men are emotionally sensitive and romantic as they are. When a relationship is rushed, the man assumes he can awake in the woman he loves, the same physical cravings he's feeling and the woman naively believes he's going to fulfill her and be tender-hearted and compassionate. Sadly enough, the only results are: unwed mothers, abandoned women, men disappointed by the coldness of their spouse and a great mutual frustration..."

I couldn't comprehend the importance of these concepts. Only after some time was I able to measure the depth of what I heard that evening. My immediate reaction was frustrated boredom. I wanted to hear how we would participate in a demonstration to attack the opposite sex.

I raised my hand and started protesting without being formally acknowledged.

"Men insist on treating us like sexual objects and then despise us for giving in. Don't you think it's time to take some action, instead of sitting here, philosophizing?"

There was absolute silence in the room, but there was a noticeable air of understanding, as if all present were looking at themselves retrospectively, in a mirror.

The doctor took a deep breath and started to answer, walking towards me.

"When we don't understand things, we think they're unfair. If women knew what I'm explaining now, they'd avoid many problems for themselves." She stopped about three feet away from me and began explaining softly yet energetically, looking at me directly as if she were a mother explaining to her daughter the definite reason for her existence. "I don't want you to take what I'm going to say, lightly, or believe that I'm stating an impractical doctrine or trying to give you a sermon."

I nodded, observing the doctor, captivated by the sound of her voice.

She continued: "We are not going to change the world here, but, in order to be happy in it, in spite of the adversity that we have faced, we will try to understand it better. All of us, since we were twelve or thirteen years old, began to menstruate, right? Well, as an adolescent, our period, far from producing any physical pleasure, was a nuisance and caused severe mood swings. Now, listen to me: Equally so, teenage boys begin to have a hormonal cycle, in which their organism rejects whatever it doesn't need. **The first difference** is that their cycle isn't periodic. It occurs unwittingly at the beginning, in so called 'wet dreams,' and afterwards it's provoked many times by themselves. **The second and more important difference** is this: The process of expelling the semen produced in their bodies causes great sexual pleasure. **For women, each menstrual cycle is an inconvenience; for men, each ejaculation is an orgasm, a physical climax, a satisfying experience.** Although a woman can be sexually excited with the right set of circumstances, she normally *has no idea* of what her brother, boyfriend or classmate has felt. She doesn't know the extent of the orgasmic pleasure that her male friends experience. It's good for girls to know from adolescence that **men will seek to repeat their very pleasurable physical experiences** and that to achieve this, *some*, **will pay money, simulate love and even force...**"

"So their glandular constitution gives them justification to rape?" I asked.

"No. Instincts do not excuse any one from assaults or humiliations. Many of those present know that frequently the motive for sexual abuse is not sex, but the brutal desire to dominate that comes from a sick person suffering emotional instability. We as women agree that the maximum punishment should be given to rapists, but we cannot label as *satanic* the normal men with whom we live. **We should, in fact, understand that their bodies have a different hormonal design, more sexual, more excitable;** that's all. Their intense erotic attraction is biologically natural from adolescence, but at the same time, **they have an identical spirit to ours, a soul similar to ours, with the same needs to accomplish goals, to serve and to reach our mission in life.**"

I looked down somewhat convinced, somewhat rebellious. After a few seconds I said:

"That sounds very logical, but, doesn't it seem to you that each person should be **responsible** for their own sexuality? The most absurd thing is to make us believe that women are responsible for the sexuality of men. Everyone says: *'He'll only go as far as she allows him to. You were raped because you were looking for it, what did you expect by getting dressed like that?'*"

"I agree," she answered. "It's unfair, but there's no need to hit our heads against the wall. For a man, to control his instincts is more bound to his spiritual and mental maturity than to his good intentions. **An immature man is, by tradition, philandering and promiscuous;** that's why we, as intelligent women, should know how to look after ourselves. Through a man's sight, he's easily stimulated and excited. **When we exhibit our sexual attributes we are visually stimulating not only those who have self-control but also those who don't.** We flirt trying to attract someone without knowing his intrinsic maturity and frequently, things get out of control. We lure men as if we were bait on a line and then we complain about being treated like sexual objects. **Sexuality is something very beautiful to be enjoyed in private with your intimate partner, in a loving environment, as a total gift.** Therefore, ***there's no need*** to exhibit publicly what you're endowed with or allow caresses when you're not completely sure of the strength and real affection of your partner."

I finally began to comprehend the message. Certainly if women were taught, from childhood, to see things the way they really are, we'd avoid many disappointments.

I looked around the room and discovered many warm and friendly faces.

"I came," I said, feeling my grief begin to envelope me again, "because I pressed charges against my offender at the prosecutor's office and they told me that I could find legal advice here."

The leader of the group stood up and walked up to me.

"You've come to the right place. Women who press charges accusing the rapist are great women, **because they're exercising their right to defend themselves** and, above all, because they're saving other women from suffering the same fate. In this group we advise, support and help those who wish to proceed legally, but **it's totally a personal decision** and we do not compel anyone to do it. We all have the right to choose the best way to recover our self-confidence. These meetings are geared to repair our self-esteem, to free ourselves from hatred, resentment, fear and the terrible burden of feeling that something irreplaceable has been taken away from us. **No one has taken anything, we are still very valuable, even more than before, since what we really are has nothing to do with our genitals, but with the purity of our hearts, the greatness of our ideas and the self-confidence of who we are.** To forgive is a liberating act and, even if you don't believe me, it's exclusive to those who are spiritually superior."

I couldn't argue with these conclusions, not just because of the kind and straightforward way they had been presented, but more importantly, because of the conviction they had implanted in me. My mind was in chaos. I looked down at my stomach and remembered the baby inside of me. My feelings toward him had changed radically after the rape. He was mine, but he was also that monster's, who I was prepared to send to prison... I felt the closeness of several of the girls that had come up to comfort me. The group would offer me help, that was evident, but they couldn't solve *all* of my problems...

10

Revenge

The pilot informed us through the tiny speaker that we had begun our descent. Soon we would be on the ground. I felt worn out and drained after hearing my wife's story.

I closed my eyes and recalled how I had met her. She was already an active member of the women's support group when by accident, while I was waiting for the meeting of Alanon, I saw her go up to the podium to say a few words.

"The truth is..." I confessed to her in a low voice, "the first time I heard you speak in public you made a tremendous emotional impact on me. You weren't a theory, the fact was you were living proof that **it was possible** to free yourself internally."

"You've never told me how you managed to hear what I said that evening in front of the group."

"It was easy. When I saw you arrive and you told me what kind of meeting it was, I remained by the door, captivated by your style. I put the book down and paced back and forth until I found a crack in the wooden partition where I planted myself discreetly and began spying on the meeting."

"You began?"

"Yes. The security guard caught me. He was upset and insisted that I wait outside until the women's group had finished. I reluctantly retreated to the street, feeling terribly confused. In a sudden rush, the threatening words from my former gang inundated my mind as cold chills forewarned me. I don't know why Alma came to my mind with such intensity, but with a sixth sense I felt certain that she was in some kind of danger. I took the city bus which dropped me off at the corner closest to my house and ran up the stairs. As soon as I put the key in the lock, my suspicions became real and I knew something was very wrong... I was greeted by a pistol pointed at my head."

Feeling the icy cylinder caress my scalp, fear penetrated my every cell. I lifted my hands desperately searching all around me, suddenly finding myself in a game of life or death.

"Walk, don't turn around."

I worriedly obeyed and mumbled: "Take whatever you want but don't hurt my family or me."

"Wha'd ya say bastard?" The thug shoved me until I stumbled falling right in front of him. "Shut up!"

I wanted to remain right there but he attacked kicking and forcing me to roll all the way down the winding staircase. He put the gun to my head again and forced me to crawl back up the stairs. In Ro's bedroom I found my invalid grandmother, lying on the floor next to her wheelchair, my uncle unconscious and my mother's hands and feet tied. I stood up more as a gesture of reproach than an attempt to defend myself, but without any warning, the handle of the gun delivered a blow to my face.

I fell like dead weight and remained immobile with my eyes closed. The assailant thought I had passed out and didn't even bother to tie me up. He took the key from the inside dead-bolt, closed the door and locked it from the outside.

Close by, my mother who couldn't move, asked me: "Are you all right?"

"Yes," I answered, sitting up slowly, "and you?"

"I'm okay."

I knelt down by her side.

"What about Dad?" I began to untie her, "and Alma?"

"Your father is in the living room. Drunk. Alma hid."

"Did you see her? Is she safe?"

"When they knocked at the door, she opened it, the three thugs pushed and entered while she moved back and ran. They grabbed me immediately, but I screamed with all my might and then Ro came down through the interior staircase to see what was going on. They beat him and dragged him here. They're armed."

I turned to look at my grandmother who was concentrating on her prayers. Her face was bent down and her hands clasped together. I'm sure she was certain that it was the only and yet the best thing that she could do.

"What do they want?"

"They asked me for money, I told them that we didn't have any."

I didn't ask her *what money* they could be talking about neither did I question if she knew where my father had put it.

"They'll search the house and, when they don't find anything, they'll leave.""

"I'm not so sure."

I wasn't either. They weren't just interested in recovering their money, they wanted revenge. I wondered why the three of them were hiding their faces when it was obvious that they were part of the gang.

"You know them, right?"

I finished untying her hands and stood up.

"They're wearing masks, Mom, how can I know who they are?"

I opened the window and grabbed the vertical steel bars that my uncle Ro had installed as protection many years before. The corrosion had detached one of them from the upper part and, with enough force, it would be possible to push it open in order to get out.

Hearing Alma's terrifying scream, I froze.

I looked at my mother.

"They've got your sister! please," she begged me, "do something...!"

I tried to separate the bars; it required much more strength than I had thought. I managed to get my head through with difficulty and then my body. I felt asphyxiated. The adrenalin helped me open them a little more and finally I was able to get out. Alma screamed again.

"My God..."

Scared to death, I felt a tingling sensation in my arms.

I had to jump to the other balcony to go in through the living room door. I examined the space that separated them. The distance between them was over three feet... The idea of a fall from that height terrified me. I had never before seen three feet that seemed like six.

Without thinking, I stepped onto the railing and jumped. It was certainly not a graceful move. I fell face down, twisting an ankle. Limping, I got to the door to discover with growing terror that it was locked. I thought of breaking the glass, but the noise would alert the assailants. I looked down the three stories and leaned over the railing to see the apartment that was exactly below me, but I couldn't tell if the door was open or not, but more than likely it was since dad liked to open it when he drank.

My sister's screams and cries made my doubts disappear. I climbed over, holding onto the railing. My legs hung in the air and a cold sweat ran down my forehead. I had to swing, holding on tight to the railing and make a dangerous leap just as my feet became aligned at the right angle. If I failed I could fall on the edge, lose my balance and find myself twenty five feet down on the pavement. I inhaled and exhaled rapidly, swung decidedly and just as I felt that my hands were slipping, I jumped. To land on the right spot was more of a miracle than ability. Many times, after this awful episode, I leaned forward to evaluate the possibility of repeating the feat and it literally seemed impossible.

I trembled listening to my sister's sobbing... I felt helpless, but at least I was closer to her. I took a steel pipe that was used to support the clothes line and full of terror pushed the sliding door. The aluminum framework opened silently and I went in. Bumping into my intoxicated father, I was filled with rage. How was it possible that when he was sober he could beat and yell at us like a tyrant, yet now when we actually needed him, he couldn't move a finger to help us.

In the hallway, the three masked gang members were pulling Alma. She kicked and punched the air while screaming. Her resistance seemed to amuse and excite the aggressors more. For a moment I was paralyzed with fear. I wasn't good at fighting one on one and even less against three. Besides, there was something ominous that took my breath away. I knew my ex-friends well, even with their masks on I could have identified them by their movements and builds. Only *one* of the three belonged to the gang, the leader himself. The other two were older and hairy, with dirty spare tires hanging over their belts.

What did this mean? I thought about begging for mercy promising that I would return what I stole and that I'd pay for my guilt, but their wicked laughs indicated that they were enjoying the holdup and at this point were not going to be moved by my pleas or reason.

I put my back against the wall and held my breath, frozen with dread, not knowing what to do. Alma saw me out of the corner of her eye and with the look on her face she begged me, implored me, to please help her.

All reason vanished.

I clutched the pipe with all my strength and ran after the leader of the gang, who was touching my sister, and pounded him on the head. I did it without holding anything back, really trying to hurt him; the blow sounded hollow, it had only grazed him. He grabbed his head and howled.

The others let Alma go and came towards me.

The first impact was a punch to the stomach that knocked the wind out of me. As I doubled up I was belted right in the face and fell on my side like a sack of potatoes, while countless red stars blinked before my eyes. I couldn't defend myself, much less attack them. The rain of blows was constant and brutal. Instinctively, I crouched over covering my neck with my arms and hands while receiving the bloodthirstiest punishment of my life. They kicked and pummeled me mercilessly again and again with the steel pipe. In the midst of the beating my mind kept repeating like a broken record *"cover your head, don't lose consciousness; everything can be healed except the brain"*. I don't know at what point the threads connecting my nervous system became overwhelmed, but I passed out and let myself drift into a deep black abyss that was calling my name.

I thought I was in another dimension, perhaps dead, because I could hear them talking and observed the scene without feeling any pain.

One thug told the other that he had shattered my eye and to leave me alone while the third insisted on shooting me once and for all.

Tell me something. Just out of curiosity. What's your name and what sort of group is this?

The young woman moved back with evident distrust on her face. She watched me cautiously and slowly answered: My name is Lisbeth and this is a support group for victims of rape.

You and your sister are a couple of pigs. You're always messing up your clothes and coming into the house full of dirt. Can't you see that I just washed the floors?

Suddenly there was an explosion, a fire on the stage, a deafening noise, and the concert began. In a collective scream, all present got up on their seats and began to scream and clap.

When I regained consciousness I was in a small white room, inside a half-destroyed body, with two fractured ribs, stitches on my head and an operation on my eye. The moment I awoke, an intense pain made me scream. Two nurses arrived quickly to administer a sedative.

Not really conscious of my misfortune, I dozed off again and the vivid dreams continued in a broken and irrelevant sequence.

We're only students.

Aren't you ashamed, you jerk? You insist on showing your student I.D. when you're really a criminal. You're not students. You're human crap. You don't even have the courage to face what you've done and you're just hiding behind the title of students...

I opened my eyes and yelled as the agony set in.

At that moment, I didn't realize that those dreams would later form a chain of nightmares that would haunt me for many years.

Where was I?

Finally recognizing the hospital room, gasping for breath with my head spinning, I felt like I was tumbling...

I have to take my sister to the support group for women. She must know that not all men are perverse so she won't drown in bitterness.

I tried to get up and go to the bathroom, but the second I moved, besides the extreme physical torture, I felt an emotional impact realizing that, in the corner of the hospital room, there was a familiar shadow watching me...

"Alma?" I asked. "Is that you? What are you doing here?"

"No one saw me when I sneaked into the room."

"Is everyone all right?"

"Yes. Only Ro got six stitches on the forehead."

I moaned as I let my head fall back on the pillow.

"I'm glad you're here."

She approached with small hesitant steps staring down at the floor.

"You saved me," she uttered.

"No..."

"You protected me. I should be the one in this hospital bed. If it wasn't for you, I would be."

"No... No..."

"You're sweating. Does it hurt a lot?"

"Stop worrying..."

"I love you."

I had never heard her say that. It was the first and last time.

Soon after, I fell asleep. The nightmares returned. Every time that I woke up trying to grab on to a less grotesque vigil, I saw my sister. Her still image, deeply disturbed by wrongly assumed guilt, appeared vaguely in between my dreams, like a background tapestry, like a subtle melody, always there. I became accustomed to her, until she became an essential part of my recovery. Later, I found out that she was able to convince the doctors to let her stay with me day and night during my long hospital recuperation. She was a nonentity in everyone's eyes; they left her alone at home too long, but this time she rebelled and preferred to stay by my side.

I had two more operations. Alma was always there. During that time I learned to love her and appreciate what it meant to have a sister, whose kindness I had never experienced before. I started to understand her fear of being useless and in everyone's way. If my self-esteem was low due to our dysfunctional family, Alma's was nonexistent. However, she made the effort to grab on to me, to help me in order to help herself, as if I was the mooring where she could tie her boat, as if my person represented her only chance for rescue in her imminent shipwreck.

One morning when she was still sleeping, I got up and looked at myself in the mirror. I was shocked at seeing my face. The bruises had not disappeared completely and the blotchy swelling gave me a monstrous appearance. I touched my cheek softly. It was me but it didn't look like me... My head was shaved where large stitches appeared in place of hair and a huge white patch covered where my left eye had been.

A wave of frustration and rage invaded me. I wanted to break the mirror, throw the table, hit the wall, but I held myself piercing my arms with my fingernails... The swelling of my face would end up disappearing, I knew that, but I was also aware that I would be left visually impaired forever.

The panic of facing my new condition numbed me as I looked at myself in the mirror.

"Why?" I muttered. "My God. This isn't fair. Damn You. I hate You... Where were You when this happened? Why did it happen?!"

My sister awoke and silently observed me.

I turned around and protested to her:

"You didn't tell me what I look like!"

"You'll recover."

"Aren't you scared when you look at me?"

"At first... But not anymore..."

I walked slowly to the bed.

"I swear to you, I'll get back at them..."

She got up without a word, walked over and embraced me. I hugged her back but without any strength as I looked over her shoulder.

The following days I hardly spoke.

They released me after almost a month in the hospital. By that time, I had a plan.

I went to the police station to look for the officers that had roughed me up when we robbed the store... I didn't know their names, so I stayed at the entrance keeping vigil for several hours, until I saw them arrive.

"Don't you recognize me?"

They delayed in reacting.

"No. Can we help you?"

"I'm one of the guys that you caught robbing the self-service store. You told me that you didn't smash my face because the parents of irresponsible losers, idiots, scum like me, tend to sue the police when they mistreated their pretty fags..."

They were speechless facing what seemed to be a reproach.

"As you can see," I continued, "someone's already smashed my face..."

"So, what do you want?"

"To get revenge. I left the gang and look what happened to me. I'll give you all the information about those who steal, rape, and assault people, but, in exchange I need you to tell me about someone who can eliminate the guy that left me without an eye."

The policemen were more frightened than interested.

"We'll catch the thugs and they'll go on trial, that's all we can do..."

"But before, I need to see the leader of the gang half-dead."

"We don't do that..."

"You don't but there has to be someone who will..."

"Sorry."

I had turned around to leave when a man came between me and my way to the door.

He whispered: “Follow me.”

I walked behind him. He was an unusual sort of man with a hard look, yet dressed in an elegant suit. He stopped on the street and said:

“I know some ex-police officers... but they’ll charge a lot...”

“Where are they?”

“Besides, you’ll get messed up in really dirty business like you won’t believe. If you get involved with the mafia, it’ll be very difficult for you to get out.”

“Where are they?”

That night I went directly to the nightclub that my supposed helper had mentioned, looking for two assasains for hire. As soon as I went in, I understood what he had implied when he said I’d step into dirty business. The place was dark and there was a foul smell. Cheap music combined with dimmed red lights gave the place a Dantesque appearance. Half-naked women danced with drunk men. I sat on a chair in the corner and felt my pants become wet. Startled, I jumped up at the same moment two guys started yelling and insulting each other. When I least expected it, I found myself witnessing a terrible brawl.

When I heard gunshots, I ran out.

On the street, I was breathing hard but determined to carry out my plan. The following day I would go back to the nightclub to look for some professional killers. I’d ask directly for them and move quickly, but I should take some money. That was essential. Where could I get it?

I thought about Don Joel and a smile illuminated my face. He’d lend it to me.....

As I adjusted my pants, I looked down at my wet hand. It hadn’t been water or wine on the chair as I had guessed. It was blood.

11
Cause and effect

The following day I went by the food processing plant, confident of how clever I was and sure that Don Joel would lend me the cash. I was dressed for serious business in my leather jacket, hat and boots since afterwards I'd go to the nightclub and finish what I had set out to do.

I identified myself to the security guard and he called on the intercom to find out if he could let me in. Joel and his father had visited me at the hospital the previous week. He agreed, glad to see me up and about. I entered the building and went rapidly towards the executive offices nervously looking around, afraid I might run into my father any moment. Fortunately I didn't. Surprised, Don Joel greeted me smiling.

"Now tell me, to what do I owe this visit? Are you feeling better?"

I shook his hand, but didn't answer his questions.

"You got me into this. It's not fair. Either you finish dragging me out of the quicksand or forget about me and leave me the way I was."

He frowned, looking puzzled as if I was speaking Chinese.

"What are you talking about?"

"You have the way to help my father yet you didn't give it to me. You motivated me to leave the gang and now look at what happened. I'm sorry, Sir. You can't just wash your hands with my life and then walk away."

"I see that you're very upset, Zahid. Why don't you have a seat?"

"No, Sir. I need you to lend me some money. I know who did this to me and I'm going to make them pay. I lost an eye, but they'll lose a lot more."

Don Joel shook his head sadly.

"What's going on? What's your plan?"

"I'm going to bravely defend my honor, like a man."

"Then don't count on me."

"Why? Aren't you able to put your advice into **action**? Encouraging words don't solve problems, you need definite plans."

"So you're looking for money to carry out your revenge?"

"That's right. Giving them what they deserve will make it very clear that no one can abuse me and get away with it!"

He watched me, visibly upset. He let a few seconds go by so that his feelings would calm down and then asked with a steady voice:

"Did you read the book that I suggested to you?"

"Yes, it talks about not letting yourself be manipulated, about defending your integrity and respect; thus, why should I have to stand still for this with my arms crossed? I'm no coward."

"Let's see," he reasoned. "You were in a traumatology hospital. Standard procedure there is that all patients who are admitted are required to make a statement explaining the cause of their accident and when the injuries are the product of third parties, like in your case, automatically the corresponding legal authorities are notified."

"Yes, but I'm not satisfied with that. Those are simple bureaucratic procedures. Surely they'll file it away. I want to be certain that what happened to me doesn't go unpunished."

Don Joel let himself fall into his executive chair with a disheartened expression. Now he seemed to be more upset than troubled.

"There's a lot of hatred behind your words," he said.

I clenched my fists.

"Yes, Sir. I'm feeling a lot of anger. I didn't deserve to be almost killed for what I did."

"What you did?"

I bit my tongue. Well, I couldn't conceal the truth anymore.

"What I did, I did motivated by you. That night you got your son and me out of jail, you severely reprimanded us, your words confused me, they made me feel like a fool, so as soon as I got out of your car I went to the gang's hideout and destroyed everything. I burned the drugs and took the money that we had stolen with the intentions of returning it."

"And, did you return it?"

I shook my head.

"My father took it away from me."

He nodded very slowly, like a judge who is on the verge of giving his verdict.

"With your revenge," he concluded, "you planted this evil and now that you are harvesting it you really want to sow it back again? When are you going to stop? Until they kill you?"

"Until it's necessary. No one makes fun of me."

Don Joel stood up and walked towards the window.

"Let's talk about things as they really are, my friend." His voice was strong and powerful. "It's a lie to talk about competing at a state fair if it's only in reference to whether you win or lose, the truth is that everyone finds what they go looking for. To press charges against your aggressor so that he pays his penalty according to the law is fine. If the legal process will give you peace of mind, go ahead, but don't go any further. Hotheaded with anger, you might overreact and go too far outside what is legally allowed and perhaps harm another person, and in the end, your aggresive actions will only turn around and hurt you causing even greater damage. Therefore, stop trying to educate the world. No one can escape this. We all pay for our mistakes. An aggressor, even if charges are not pressed against him, condemns himself the moment he commits the crime. Actions and reactions are mechanisms to which we're all linked. For each one of our responses there is a resulting effect from life. Evil is sown with EVASION **(laziness, addictions, irresponsibility)**, DECEIT **(lies, thefts, gossip, adulteries)**, EXASPERATION **(anger, violence, helplessness)** and SELF-WORSHIP **(vanity, pride, arrogance)**. There are four letters: *'E.D.E.S..'* They're very easy to remember. However, 'beware' with red lights flashing the warning because these attitudes should be avoided at all cost since the person who practices them will suffer the consequences that he deserves. That's for certain!"

"And this?" I said, pointing to my face without being able to hold back the tears of frustration that escaped both my healthy eye as well as the empty socket, "don't tell me that robbing money and destroying a few things deserves *this*?"

"The part that deserved it, you received. The additional part that they took from you, life will take away from them and will give it back to you. The concept of checks and balances is unavoidable. Right now you can't understand it, but in a few years you will."

"That night I got out of your car motivated! I wanted to be different!"

"Then, why did you go back to the gang's hideaway to avenge evil with evil?"

"Because I remembered when I was a victim of insults and cruel put downs."

"And so, you wanted to get back at them by doing even greater damage? Refusing to participate with them would have been enough!"

"But I'd have to face their abuse again."

"Rather inexpensive, don't you think, compared to your broken body? Sooner or later they would have forgotten you."

"When I destroyed their hideout, I did it anonymously."

Don Joel let out a sarcastic guffaw.

"Are you saying that you didn't want to be identified? Please! Anonymity is the mark of fools and cowards! Anyone who doesn't respect himself enough to show his face, doesn't deserve to be heard. To hide behind a group, a mask, a paper without a signature, indicates that the person doesn't support his own ideas or actions, nor does he want to suffer the consequences of what he despicably does. However, the results of our actions cannot be avoided even if you go and hide at the ends of the earth. Sooner or later, everything comes to the surface. Don't ever do something you would be ashamed of."

"The jerks who beat me," I complained, "were masked... They're cowards! They should be punished!"

"Zahid. Understand this once and for all. The person who doesn't know the law of **cause and effect**, DOES NOT KNOW HOW TO LIVE: '*Every action carries its own price or punishment. Whatever you do will remain engraved in your frame of reference and eventually will result in a positive or negative reaction. Chance does not exist, everything is* ***causative****. The effect can result many years after the cause occurred, but for certain it will come out and, the longer it*

---

[1] Ralph Waldo Emerson. Essay about Compensation. Referred to by Napoleon Hill in "Grow Rich with Peace of Mind". Diana Editorial.

takes to come, whether it's positive or negative, the stronger it will be.'[1] Has someone tried to ruin your reputation? cheated you? robbed you? mistreated you? injured you? **Don't hold grudges.** Do you see the unjust people at the top of the hill and the righteous at the bottom? Don't worry. The waters sooner or later will reach their level and each person will end up exactly where they should be. Now understand this: some effects do not occur in our lifetime. Jesus was crucified and that was not the effect of His faults, but **the chain is not interrupted with physical death,** it continues and each one ends up in the place that he deserves."

"Are you saying that God allows us to suffer in order to grow?"

"Suffering originates from violating the laws. Imagine listening to a naive person who was hurt by jumping off a roof like 'Superman' and then claiming: *Why is this happening to me, my God? Why are You letting me suffer like this, why me...?* It would seem illogical to us, isn't it true? Something like this happened to you. God is not absent nor does He ignore your pain. He is with you, but UNDERSTAND this: He acts as any intelligent father would with his son who has erred. Deep inside he understands that it's better for his son to suffer from these experiences now, so he learns to be careful and avoids worse consequences in the future, but at the same time he would make sure his son feels his presence and love."

I recalled when I was complaining in front of the mirror at the hospital... Those were very hard concepts to digest and accept. They destroyed my reasons for revenge and humbled me. This meant that, in spite of my mistakes, He was there, offering me His fatherly embrace, His unconditional love and the immeasurable care of a Father...

I sat down on a chair. Don Joel came closer and put his hand on my shoulder.

"There's nothing that will wear you out more than being involved in disputes with others. It diminishes your strength, it distracts you... it makes you stagnate... You're a good man... and good men don't get into fights for revenge. Get out of that vicious circle. You don't belong in it. You have the wings of an eagle. You are more than a winner... Accept the love God is bringing into your life. Only through His power will you be able to fly..."

I lowered my head and covered my face allowing the tears to flow. Finally, I regained a little more composure and said:

"I'm so confused... each time I talk with you, your way of thinking blows me away, I don't know how to handle or react to all of this information that you bombard me with." I paused to look at him. "If I don't avenge myself, at least tell me how to compensate everything wrong that surrounds me. Is it possible to help my father?"

"Yes, to start, you and your family should stop giving in to him."

"Is that what they did to you?"

"That's right. All of a sudden my wife ignored me. When I came home drunk she didn't yell at me nor was she annoyed, she greeted me calmly and told me everyday that SHE LOVED ME ANYWAY, but that if I did something wrong, I would have to pay for my own mistake. Whenever I became stubborn, she would leave with the children and didn't pay attention to what happened to me; she said that she was only protecting her mental health and that our lives would go back to normalcy when I sought help."

"If you stop giving in and catering to others, does that allow the law of cause and effect then to take its course?"

"Well said," he applauded. "That's exactly it: **don't interfere between the cause and the natural consequences that will affect the other person, let him suffer these on his own,** for his own good and yours. **The world is full of "enablers" who give in too quickly. Kind people who are shortsighted and insist on overprotecting their loved ones, feeling sorry for them, caring for them so that they don't suffer any discomfort, keeping them from growing up.** The greatest revolutionaries in education have based their theories on this elemental concept: Allow the child to be responsible for his own choices so he will learn to measure the consequences of his actions and he will become an independent **person** and not a trained animal...! Starting today, you must stop pampering and giving in!"

"It makes sense," I said, wiping my face with a kleenex I took from the bookcase, "but how do you get the closed-minded man to suffer the consequences of his foolishness?"

"I'm going to share with you what they did to me: when they arrested me, no one ran to the police station to bail me out; if they locked me up, I would wake up in jail; if I had a car accident, I faced the police by myself; if I vomited or messed in my pants, I cleaned up after myself; if I passed out on the ground in my front yard, no one went to rescue me. My wife stopped helping at work, looking after my paperwork and justifying me in front of others. She began to sell bag lunches at schools in order to earn a living and allowed me to fall into financial ruin. When I was sober, they all showed me their love with thousands of kind details, but they stopped being affected by my addiction or feeling sorry for me even if I got into deep trouble. Only in this way was I able to understand that I needed to change."

"Sir, if what you're saying works, then I'm sure I'm not here by chance. Perhaps it's the right time to help my family take this positive next step. I understand the first two steps to help the closed-minded person are: ***To free oneself internally and to stop giving in to self-indulgence.*** What is the third?"

"The third one is called ***Loving Confrontation***. One day, my six year old daughter embraced me crying and said she was very sad because I'd killed her bunny rabbit when I kicked it, but that she still loved me; it was at that moment my heart broke. I didn't even remember doing it. **The loving confrontation is an extremely powerful resource. It's confronting a person that's lying with one other person or others who have the proof of what is really the truth.** In a loving environment, those most affected confront the *closed-minded* person, face to face, explaining clearly what happens and the *actual* consequences of his actions in their lives. The more people who participate in a planned confrontation, the better the outcome. Bosses, personnel, friends and family can collaborate; all gathered and in agreement on what each one will say, explaining how they have been affected by the conduct of the *closed-minded* person and urge him to seek help immediately. Those who might have a tendency to accuse or who are resentful shouldn't participate as well as those who aren't strong enough to stand a tense discussion, and anyone who isn't able to understand that an alcoholic is a sick person who needs help."

Only imagining a confrontation with Dad made my hands start to shake.

"If the relatives *free themselves internally, if they stop giving in to his self-indulgence and practice loving confrontations,* will the alcoholic become cured?"

"No. Remember that he has **TWO** illnesses. At that point, the first sickness will be contained: the *closed-mindedness*, but there's still the alcoholism. Then, he'll need to be admitted to a rehabilitation clinic and attend Alcoholics Anonymous meetings until he completes the group's twelve steps. Only then will the second illness be healed."

A wild idea struck me.

"Did you know that my father works here?"

He watched me with a slight smile on his face.

"Yes."

"Do you know him?"

"I'm his boss."

This was perfect! Don Joel had to be present in the loving confrontation with my father too.

"I don't want you to lend me money anymore. Now what I really need from you is something much more important. Could you come to my house and talk to my family?"

"You need to understand a confrontation is planned, it's rehearsed, and it's done after having completed the first two steps. You're still giving in and catering to your father. You're not prepared and if we do it unexpectedly, it can be counter-productive."

"All right, all right, I only want you to talk with my family... I suppose all the close relatives should be involved since as soon as the alcoholic feels unprotected by those who cater to his needs and give in to his addictions, then he'll seek someone else. Alma and my mother need to tune their ideas into the same channel... I doubt that I could convince them as well as you could."

Getting up from his chair, he looked at me with fatherly affection.

Knowing I now had the information to change my many mistakes into successes, excitement filled with hope made me realize I was finally not just full of plans and projects, but of positive actions. Walking ahead of Don Joel, my mind began planning a trap to force a confrontation with my Mom, Dad, Alma and Don Joel. Little did I know it would result in being one of the most intense experiences of my life.

12

A loving confrontation

"Hi, Mom," I said, greeting her with a kiss, "this is Don Joel, the father of a friend."

"I already had the pleasure. I met you at the hospital. Please, have a seat."

"Thanks."

"Would you like something to drink?"

"No, thank you."

"Alma!" I yelled, "come here, please!"

My sister left her room and stood by my side.

"Don Joel has come to talk to us," I explained, "he's taught me some techniques to help Dad acknowledge his need to change so I invited him to explain them to both of you."

There was total silence. The two women showed interest.

"Well," he began, slightly inhibited, "I'm a recovered alcoholic and although I know that the problems of a family like yours are very complex, someone needs to take the first step. There are certain groups for family members which all of you could attend and books that you should..."

"Tell them about the confrontation," I asked, interrupting him.

"It's one of the last and more effective steps that you'll have to take. It should take place always in the presence of a therapeutic expert. It is a prepared and rehearsed meeting where the addicted person is invited to listen to the most important people in his life, in order to show him how his addiction is damaging each one of them."

"Is it like an ultimatum?" asked mom.

"In a certain way, but it's done in an atmosphere of love and understanding, the alcoholic should not feel attacked. For that reason, everything should be well thought out ahead of time."

"Are there any specific rules to follow in a confrontation?" I asked.

"Each participant openly testifies with one or two examples of the alcoholic's disgraceful behavior. It's forbidden to state declarations of guilt such as: 'We can't stand you anymore because you've destroyed our lives.' Instead, you have to state *concrete* examples of conduct which perhaps he doesn't even remember, for instance: 'At your niece's wedding, after you drank too much, you insulted a woman and challenged her husband to a fight, and since then no one in the family will speak to us.' That is *concrete* evidence. It's not about judging or condemning but about his realizing once and for all, as a whole, what alcohol has driven him to do."

"Can we do it today?"

"No. Be patient. Everything in its own time."

"But, why wait? We understand everything. Right, Alma? Right, Mom?"

"I've participated in several confrontations," explained Don Joel, "and it's definitely not a game. There are alcoholics that, when they see all of their family and friends gathered together, believe that they are all in a conspiracy against him and react so violently that it provokes even more damaging results."

We heard some noises coming from the lock in the door.

"It's Dad," my sister said, terrified.

No one spoke for a few minutes. Far away, we could hear buses traveling on the main street.

My father came in to find his boss, wife and children all seated in the living room. He was astonished seeing us gathered together expectantly.

"Goo... good evening, is there something wrong?"

No one said anything.

"No," said Don Joel, "I just came to visit Zahid to see how he's feeling."

Dad calmed down and sat in front of him.

"I haven't been able to go to work this week," he confessed, excusing himself. "I haven't been feeling very well."

I knew this was the crucial moment. I had to get the ball rolling. There was nothing more to lose, but we had everything to gain.

"Don Joel has come to speak to us about that too." I ventured with a shaky voice. "You were an outstanding salesman once but now you're almost out of the company... Dad, we love you very much, but we believe that you don't realize what happens when... you drink..."

He took a few seconds to piece together and understand the meaning of my broken phrases. Our guest glared at me obviously annoyed. Mom was very nervous and stared at the floor while my father looked around guessing at all the probable reasons for the unexpected meeting.

"I certainly hope you're not planning on giving me a collective sermon at this stage in my life."

No one answered. It was the decisive moment. Don Joel hesitated in his decision, but finally supported me.

"Your children are especially sensitive this evening, I believe you need to hear them. Could you give them that gift?"

My father's face hardened and without showing the slightest indication of agreement, directed his penetrating eyes on me. I had the ball again. Cautiously, I mentally reviewed the basic rules of confrontation: *To state concrete evidence, showing genuine love, without arguments or changing the subject, to persist cornering the addicted person until he understands that he needs help...*

"Don't take me wrong, I'm not blaming you for this," I said, pointing to my eye, "but when the thugs broke into our house you were drunk. They were on the verge of raping my sister right in front of you. Furthermore, they came to recover their money but I couldn't return it because you had taken it from me when you were drunk with your friends, the night that they were dancing half-naked in the living room."

My father was paralyzed with shock. His boss's presence tied his hands and shut his mouth to his usual violent explosions. Everyone remained still. A slight smirk appeared on my father's overwrought flushed face.

"Are you trying to ridicule me? This is a joke, right?"

My mom looked up. I was afraid she would start apologizing for my outburst, but fortunately I was wrong.

"No, dear," she said, "we're here to tell you how much we love you and... to share with you how much alcohol... affects us all."

"You too? You better stop this. I'm warning you."

Mom was visibly disturbed by her husband's threat and looked at me out of the corner of her eye, but there was no going back. She closed her eyes slightly as if she had decided to throw caution to the wind and said:

"Six months ago, coming back from a party you were drunk and drove way over the speed limit. Your children and I were very scared. I begged you not risk our lives, but you were so angry that you stopped the car in the middle of the highway, opened the door and forced me to get out. I saw how you drove away, you couldn't even drive in a straight line. I started walking down the street, crying, truly believing I would never see my family alive again."

Dad stood up pacing around in circles. He looked like an enraged beast that doesn't know who to attack first.

"You're a sick woman," he snarled, seething through his teeth. "You exaggerate everything."

In a little mousey voice, Alma began to bravely speak:

"Sometimes when you get drunk... you mess in your pants, then... I have to clean it... Uncle Ro comes and carries you to the bedroom. He says he can look after us but I don't think... that's right..."

She didn't say anything else. I admired her effort.

"We love you very much," I intervened, "but we're scared of you. When you drink no one knows how you're going to react. Five years ago, while leaving our apartment drunk, I tried to stop you and you pushed me down the stairs. I fractured my wrist and had a cast on for ninety days."

"Besides all of this, dear," said Mom, with more self-assurance, "we've lost all of our savings, the house is mortgaged, the car is smashed up in the garage and we don't have any money to fix it. Your salary is based on the commissions you make from your sales and it's been more than three months since you've brought home a cent. Your brother supports us... Even Alma has worked at his video store for two years, trying to repay him a little for everything that he's done for us."

These were concrete arguments. My father couldn't refute them for long.

"You, as a matter of fact, used to be a valuable employee," said Don Joel, coming to our rescue, "but we've been withdrawing your responsibilities and reducing your workload. In fact, the company is on the verge of firing you. We never know when we can count on you. Alcohol is destroying you, Mr. Duarte. Your neurons are more damaged than you're aware of; this affects your brain permanently, your liver is putrefying, your kidneys are becoming weak, your testicles are shriveling up day by day until you'll become impotent."

My father sought support from the back of the armchair, breathing rapidly, as if he didn't have enough air. He didn't look up for quite a while. I'm sure that facing this sudden stress, his physical need screamed out to him, demanding a drink.

"All right," he finally said, "I admit I have some problems with drinking *now*, but eight years ago, when I didn't drink, everyone used me. When I arrived home I felt out of place, like an intruder, no one waited up for me, no one cared about me."

Don Joel had warned me: *The closed-minded person softens the hearts of the people that are close to him and pushes them to believe that they're guilty of his mistakes. Afterwards, when the same people feel overwhelmed, he then turns sweet and tender, creating emotional confusion.*

"You're avoiding the truth," stated Mom, "who cares about what happened eight years ago? We have a problem today. The main thing is to repair the present and plan for the future."

"Wait a minute. No way. You've all agreed to gang up on me but I have the right to speak too."

His voice sounded sincere. He really seemed ready to tell his side of the story.

"During those years, it probably would have been easier to stay sober if I had had a *wife*, but the woman that I lived with was a *mother*, not a *wife*." He turned to look at her with fury in his eyes. "You lived for the children. You didn't even let fresh air touch them. You were a hypochondriac and you made your children the same. You constantly thought that they were sick and stuffed them with medicine without first consulting a doctor. You made them dependent, lazy and spoiled rotten. The compulsive way in which you tended to them, the way you always paid attention to their nagging, their incessant temper tandrums and demands for what they wanted to eat, and even how you cleaned up after them when they dirtied themselves just to get attention. It all made me understand that you were an obsessive mother, a tormented prisoner without a real personality: a woman that was not a wife or a friend, and of course, not a lover. I didn't mean anything to you. You ignored me. You looked for me, extending your hand and giving me a cynical smile, only when you needed money." He interrupted himself, visibly agitated. He looked like a man that was trying to reveal all the pain hidden in his heart. "I felt used," he continued, "surrounded by phoney affection that was only interested in my money. Tired, terribly tired of working and making money only for the rest of you to enjoy, realizing I had no other option since I refused to be sucked into the complete absorption of your sick idea of what *motherhood* was all about, I concluded that my only alternative was to simply watch as you molded my children into brats. Listen to me well, and I'm not drunk. In one of those moments in which I didn't want to leave the house to go to work, and yet I didn't feel welcome in it either, I caught a glimpse of the kind of depression that can lead a lost soul to end his own life... It was then that I started drinking."

My mother seemed clearly astonished by what she was hearing.

"I found shelter in the children to avoid your chauvinism," she defended herself, "before you started drinking."

They were both right. **There had been marital problems and mutual evasions.** After he lost control of his drinking and became dependent (which he has not admitted to this date) my mother, seeing her family become more than she could relate to, found her escape by turning her obsessive love into the conduct of an indulgent martyr.

"Nothing changes from digging up the past," she insisted. "You have to stop getting drunk, now."

"Enough! Don't say it again. I can stop drinking whenever I please."

"Then do it now!"

"All that you have to do is go to a detoxification clinic," said Don Joel. "They're specialists. They'll hclp you in every way possible..."

"There's nothing to rebuild, it's too late. Besides, a clinic like that must cost a lot of money and I don't have any. Aside from my problem, we're living in an economic crisis, where sales have gone way down. The recession is really bad, making people very aggressive."

"You're right," Don Joel stood up and started walking decisively around while he continued saying: "All of us in our country feel betrayed, infuriated and have taken revenge any way we could, but we have to stop it now. We don't gain anything by fighting with our neighbor, threatening our friends, attacking our spouse, hurting our children or drowning ourselves in our own personal addictions. Times of crisis produce a tremendous increase in prostitution, pornography, drugs, alcohol, adultery, divorces, etc. Disheartened people *evade* their problems falling into a vicious circle of blaming and hurting others because this has been done to them, avoiding the real problem themselves. We have to stop this now. The real danger of an economic crisis is that it ends up affecting our family life; it's imperative to be mature enough in order to prevent ourselves from falling into harmful escapes... and if we've already fallen, we have to get up... Mr. Duarte, you *have to* get up. Do it for your children. You can put an end to the negative events that continue to snowball affecting your whole family. They're simply asking you for help. That's all."

For the first time my father's face became broken and humble. He was staring off into space and his mouth was closed tight, with his lips sticking out.

"Dad," my sister approached him, trembling. "Please listen to what they're telling you. I need you more than you'll ever know. I have no one to confide in or help me with my problems."

Alma put her arms around Dad's waist and started crying wholeheartedly, with the accumulated tears from years of bitterness. It was at that precise moment when Dad finally broke.

"What do I have to do?" he asked.

"There is a detoxification clinic that you'll have to check into tomorrow morning. The company will take care of the expenses. Everything has already been taken care of," Don Joel lied. "Think of it as a vacation for a couple of weeks. Then you'll go back to your normal activities and attend AA meetings every week."

My mother had recovered her self-assurance and added:

"I admit the mistakes that I made," she said. "If you accept this treatment, you can count on me, I'll be a real wife, the companion that you need..." her determined face revealed an expression of firmness, "but *if you don't look after your problem*, nothing will change, except..." she made a brief pause to take a breath before declaring: "You'll be a lot more lonely than before because... I refuse to continue living with you like this."

"Are you threatening me?"

She held her stance staring directly at him and Dad realized that it was not a threat nor a game, it was a reality.

"All right... I'll do what you're asking me, but I'll go when I want to."

Mom shook her head. Alma continued crying inconsolably.

"It's now or never..."

He looked down at the floor and nodded only once.

Alma and I helped Mom prepare Dad's suitcase. He also helped, distracted, without adding anymore to what had already been said... You could sense opposing emotions strangely vibrating in the atmosphere of our house; sadness and joy at the same time; fear and adventure; as if in the blackest jungle, you could vaguely see far off in the distance encouraging beams of light.

Soon after, we got a call from Don Joel, telling us that, *then*, everything had been arranged and that he would pick up my father very early the next morning.

I tried to sleep that night but I couldn't. I felt nervous from so many stimulating and exciting events which were difficult to assimilate. Silently, I walked out of my room to go and talk to my sister. She always locked her door. I knocked.

"Are you awake?"

She took a while to answer, but finally opened the door and then went back to sit down on her bed. I stayed at the door.

"Are you all right?"

"Yes...Come in."

"I can't sleep."

"I can't either."

"I want to talk to you."

I felt like she wasn't listening.

"I admire you a lot," she said to me.

"Thanks Alma, but I need to share with you everything I've learned lately."

"Have you ever felt that you're useless?"

"What are you talking about?"

"I don't know... but sometimes I feel like that. Stupid, not wanting to live."

I studied her silently. It was a non-connected conversation. Was she trying to tell me something?

She lay back on her pillow and seemed pensive as she looked up at the ceiling.

"The world is a bunch of crap..."

"What's gotten into you? Aren't you supposed to be happy because of what happened today? Besides, you're a good person. I'm very grateful to you for the way you looked after me at the hospital. We're friends. You can trust me."

"And what do I gain by that?"

"Alma, tell me what's on your mind. I want to help you."

She shook her head.

"It's nothing special... I'm just depressed."

"But you're *always* depressed!"

"Did you come here to scold me?"

"No, no..." I interrupted myself without knowing how to break the barrier. "There are certain places where people who have similar problems to ours, get together. I read a very important book that you must read... You're responsible for yourself. You need to have more courage and strength to search for solutions. It's a lie that you're stupid or useless. And you can't be depressed all the time."

"Are you talking about the place where kids meet who have alcoholic parents?"

"Yes. I also know a group where women who are victims of rape meet."

She glanced up with interest. I felt motivated for having awoken a certain curiosity in her, and excitedly continued:

"I listened to a woman who had been raped. She spoke in front of a group and said to them: '*Before I used to feel sorry for all the people that suffer. Today I only feel sorry for those who suffer in ignorance and don't understand the essential usefulness of pain.*[1] *I was raped and yet, I want to tell you that such a terrible experience has broadened my views about life, it has made me more mature, more of a woman, and above all, more deserving of love. It might seem strange, but when you fall into the quicksand, your life changes radically, for the good or for the bad. If you allow yourself to feel hopeless, neurotic and full of self-pity, inevitably you're bound to sink. If, instead, you fight against the idea of sinking, looking for God, the only Superior Entity there is, clinging to His love and forgiveness, filling yourself with His endless energy, then you'll have the courage and strength to forge ahead and, achieving this, you'll be a different person. If you feel life has no meaning, that your problems are destroying you, memorize this parable:* ***A bird that lived in the hollow of a tree in the middle of a swamp had resigned himself to being there; he ate the worms***

1. Bill W. "*The Path of life*". Selections of writings by the co-founder of A. A.

from the marsh and was always dirty from the stagnated mud. His wings were useless because of the weight from the dirt, until one great gust of wind destroyed his shelter; the rotten tree sank into the quicksand and he realized he was going to die. In a sudden rush to save himself, he started desperately flapping his wings in order to fly. This was very hard for him because he had forgotten how to fly, but he confronted the pain from the stiffness until he managed to rise and cross the wide sky, finally arriving at a fertile and beautiful forest. *Serious problems are like the gust of wind that has destroyed your shelter and is forcing you to fly..."*

"Or to die..."

"Listen. You're not going to die. Neither am I. Dad will become rehabilitated. This family will be normal again..."

"Did you really hear all of that or are you making it up?"

The way that she kept changing the conversation confused me, it seemed as if she couldn't concentrate on one thing.

"I heard it eavesdropping outside of the women's meeting."

"I spend too much time alone. I liked the confrontation but maybe nothing will come of it. Uncle Ro is the only one who understands me. I really don't know why I feel like this. I wish I were more like you."

What did one phrase have to do with the other? I truly thought that there was something wrong with my sister's mind. I raised my voice trying to force her to pay attention to me. I needed to tell her very clearly what would happen:

"Alma, listen. Today I made a decision to change my life. I was ready to take revenge and keep falling into the pit but I made a definite decision not to. I'll soon finish high school and I'm going away to college. It's the only way I'll be able to develop myself on my own. I'm willing to pay the price to become successful. I have to, do you understand me? I've made lots of mistakes and I've decided to change. But you also have to decide to climb out of your own depression. You have to force yourself to meet positive people, read self-improvement books, listen to conferences... Brush off the apathy... I don't want to leave you alone, not like this."

I sat next to her. She turned slightly and I caught a glimpse, that was almost imperceptible, of some obscure perversity in her eyes. She was a thirteen year old girl! No. I shook my head. For sure I must have misinterpreted her look because of the faint light from the lamp.

"Will you do it?" I asked, "if we separate, do you promise that you'll do it? I'll keep in touch with you, but..."

She interrupted me, hugging me with all her strength.

However, the burden of too many traumas had taken their toll on her weak constitution... Sadly, I didn't realize this until many years later.

13

Adoption

The plane was about to land.

"What went wrong?"

"I don't know."

"Did you speak to her after that night?"

"Several times... She wouldn't listen to me, she always seemed lost in her unknown fantasies... I shared all that I had learned. In a way, I became a nagging brother trying to teach her, but in the end, she would invariably reject me. When she saw me coming, her face changed into a mocking smirk and she'd ask me if I was going to give her another moralistic sermon... Ideas make you free or a slave. You can hold onto positive ideas as if they were branches from a tree offering you a way out from the quicksand that is pulling you under into the mire. She had those concepts within her reach, but she didn't try to grab onto them to escape."

"Why? What was the mistake?"

"I don't know. Lisbeth, you're a woman, help me to understand. I realize you've told me this before, but I need to hear it again. How did you overcome the trauma of rape and your pregnancy? You did something that Alma couldn't or didn't want to do."

The plane landed and we left politely saying good-bye to the pilot.

I looked at my watch.

As we had calculated, it was almost one o'clock in the morning. We entered the airport through a narrow door used exclusively by the passengers of private planes and ran to the taxi counter.

"Where are you going?" the clerk asked.

I gave him the name and address of the hospital that I had obtained over the phone. He gave me a ticket, indicating the amount to pay.

We went immediately to the car that was waiting for us. In the taxi, on our way to the hospital, she began to relate her story once again.

After my initial meeting with the support group, an attorney approached me offering to represent my case for a minimal fee, so I set up an appointment with her to further discuss the details of my law suit. When the meeting ended and it was time to leave, all of the women warmly said their good-byes to me. Some offered me their personal cards and others invited me to parallel groups related to their religion: prayer groups, Bible studies and evangelical gatherings.

They explained to me that all the support groups have the same principles, based on the twelve steps of Alcoholics Anonymous.

In an abbreviated form, they are:

THE <u>NEED</u> TO ADMIT that we are helpless when we face certain events and emotions.

THE <u>CONVICTION</u> that only God, the Superior Entity, can restore our destroyed life.

THE <u>DECISION</u> of giving our will to that Superior Power.

THE <u>RESTITUTION</u> of righting the wrong to the people we hurt because of our lack of self-control.

THE <u>COMMITMENT</u> to help new people who are trapped in a similar problem.

Recovering from my depression was like learning how to walk again. The job demanded all of my time and effort. I attended all the meetings that they invited me to and I followed each step to the "T": I stopped judging others and gossiping, adamantly protesting when others would put me down. I began reading self-improvement and spiritual books daily, accumulating a vast collection in addition to listening to cassettes about how to become successful; in other words, I changed my *mental food.* I had these principles to work with and by assimilating all of these new concepts, my way of thinking began to change and I gradually developed a tremendous strength of character. **When you change what you eat, you change what you are. The mind is fed with concepts. In the end, our personal frame of reference is made of those ideas that we continually feed into our mind.**

This new way of thinking helped me face the trial against Martin and his two accomplices.

However, my misfortune was soon out in the open. All of my friends and relatives found out about the problem. The press was very hard on me and the tabloids ate it up. Some headlines read: *"Revenge or indifference?", "Women take revenge", "Raped young girl sues the rapist but decides to have his baby".* This last headline was accompanied by a series of commentaries where my version was put in question. *"If what the girl says were true, she wouldn't tolerate giving birth to a product from one of the rapists. We found out through a good source that she was his girlfriend and had an active sex life with him, so possibly the suit is a result more of a gilted lover than a rape."*

If I hadn't had the group's support, I might not have been able to endure so much abuse from the press. Above all because part of it was true.

Exactly as they had warned me, the trial was long and draining.

After one of the most wearing sessions, Martin caught up with me and maliciously threatened me:

"You're a prostitute. You'll see what's going to happen to your baby. He'll always be the weak link that connects you to me..."

I left the hearing in tears. My psychology teacher was by my side.

"This is so hard!" I said to her, "with everything that's happened, I'm more convinced than ever that Martin is crazy. I'm sure that sooner or later he'll reappear to claim his paternity and take revenge on our child."

"Very soon he'll be in jail."

"But someday he'll get out... Besides, how will I explain this to my child when he grows up?"

The teacher thought about it and after a while she said to me:

"You have to search out all of your possible choices before you decide what to do. **Solutions don't arrive at anyone's door, one must go out and seek them.**"

"What do you suggest?"

"A good friend of mine is the director of a children's shelter. I'd like you to talk with him."

"Don't even think of it!" You're insane if you think I'd abandon my child in a place like that."

"It's not one of those..."

"Then?"

"Just come with me."

As I previously mentioned, I tried to keep an open mind, so the following day I went with my psychology teacher to the shelter.

Her friend ended up being a very friendly physician. With two social workers he showed me the facilities of a building that was something between a school and a low class hotel. The collective dormitories were austere, the beds were worn out, small and crammed together. The bathrooms were dirty and in need of repair. Dozens of children followed us as if each visit was a party for them. I noticed something unusual and asked:

"Do you have any babies?"

"A few. They're easily adopted."

"The older children are rejected?"

"Actually, the situation is worse. They're here in custody but they can't be adopted because their real parents periodically come in to sign an affidavit so they won't lose their parental rights. Some children grow up and run away, others visit their home from time to time and return beaten, drugged or sexually molested..."

Before entering the offices, a little girl who was barely five, stopped in front of us offering me a dirty ribbon as a gift. Seeing her broke my heart and I embraced her. She was filled with happiness and skipped away.

"She can't be adopted either?" I asked.

"No. Her legal situation prevents it. The mother refuses to relinquish her custody. These children have been denied the option of having a home." The doctor walked towards a filing cabinet and pointed to it. "On the other hand, there are many couples with economic stability, spiritual and emotional maturity that cannot have children; they'd be excellent parents. Many have been waiting a long time for a baby, but when you talk about adoption to the biological mothers, they get offended. Most of the people, even men, are so possessive and egotistical that they prefer to see their children dead than with another family."

"Don't you think that's an exaggeration?"

"My friend, are you forgetting that legal abortion is the preferred option? Millions of children are killed every year in this way. The parents act like owners of their children, they abuse them, asphyxiate them, prevent them from growing up normally and prefer to leave them in physical and mental misery rather than flourishing and learning to be independent. Obsessive love and selfishness are the main enemies in the development of normal children."

"I'm pregnant," I confessed, "and very confused..."

"I know, they've already explained your case to me; you're a seventeen year old single mother. If you decide to abort, you'll be choosing the cowardly way out by avoiding the fact that by taking what seems to be the easiest route, you'd be definitely killing another human being."

"I'm not thinking of doing that," I defended myself immediately, "I feel the baby growing inside of me. I couldn't kill him even if his father were the worst man on earth. There are many people with fathers who are addicts or dysfunctional, but that doesn't take away their right to live."

"Well said; eliminating that, only a few options are left: if you decide to raise your child alone, it will be a very commendable sacrifice, but it will be difficult to erase your bitter memories everytime you look at him. Without a doubt, because of your age, your parents will end up intervening and you'll probably delegate to them your child's care and education. The last alternative...", he stopped and every fiber of my being resisted hearing what was obvious, "is to give him up for adoption. That would demand from you an even greater sorrow and heartache than the other two, above all because you wouldn't be doing it to avoid the problem, but because you know that the child will be growing up in a stable home, with a father, mother, cousins, grandparents, etcetera; that he'll be with people who will adore him and want him very badly; and the truth is he'll be better off than he'd be with you."

The option was logical, but my heart rebelled.

"I know many mothers that have been able to bring up their children without a father, which to me is much more admirable!"

"I agree. Motherhood can make a woman outstanding and inspiring, however, this doesn't always happen. You could become a martyr, pathetically trying to manage alone with your child. However, inevitably both of you will end up burning at the stake. Or, you could maturely decide to love your child so much that **you're willing and have the capacity to allow him to live separated from you but in a normal and happy family...** This is what real love is all about, not some romantic ideals that masquerade selfishness."

One of the social workers spoke, supporting the doctor.

"It would be like saying to your child: *I love you so much that I'll do anything for you, even deny myself the joy of seeing you forever, if that is what's best for you."*

The room became a frozen painting. They were all watching me in silence. I stared at the floor but after a few minutes, I grabbed at the only objection I could find:

"An adopted child sooner or later finds out and becomes angry at his real mother because she gave him up for adoption."

"Perhaps, but the trauma is easily overcome because by then, he's already sure of who he is and what he believes in."

"So then, the best solution for all single mothers is to give up their children for adoption?"

"No. Every situation is different and must be analyzed separately. In yours especially, I believe it would be the best scenario for you."

"You're saying that because you're a man."

"Men are objective, women emotional. Both sexes should seek a happy medium. Life would be a lot easier if men were more sensitive and women more impartial."

My teacher put her arm around me and whispered, as if we were alone:

"We've come solely to hear the options. I'm sure you'll make the right decision when you calmly balance all the choices. Would you like to meet with women who have had abortions so they can tell you firsthand how they felt after having had one?"

"No, thanks. I can imagine."

"Then, with women who have faced the problem alone or have given custody to the grandparents, pretending for the rest of their life to be the child's older sister...?"

I stood still, my mind was in chaos and, unintentionally, a few tears rolled down my cheeks.

"That must be extremely painful," I reflected. "Not to be able to embrace your own child or say to him: 'son, I love you'; to have him grow up far from your guidance and authority... Thanks, but I'm not crying because I feel pressured or because I lack information, I'm crying because I believe I've already made up my mind and realizing what I have to do is breaking my heart."

The physician concluded:

"If your child were diagnosed with a terrible disease and the only way to save him was to take a very bitter medicine, would you do it?"

I nodded.

A medicine to save him. I had never looked at it that way.

"What do I have to do?"

"Don't feel pressured."

"I'm not," I insisted, "what's the next step?"

The director of the center requested something from one of the social workers that I couldn't understand. She left the office but returned later bringing with her a voluminous file. The doctor looked through it quickly and handed it to me:

"These are copies of the information gathered about parents that wish to adopt a newborn baby. Go through them. If you're really sure, choose a couple with the religion, customs, age, profession, pastimes, activities and personality that seems the best and closest to who you are. You have over thirty options. All of them are excellent. In the file you won't find addresses or complete names since the process is anonymous and confidential. They won't know who you are nor will you meet them. Once the adoption has taken place, even if you regret it later on, it will be very hard to locate your child."

"How terrible..." I murmured, taking the file.

My pain was deep, but my love was deeper.

I told my parents about my decision. In another context perhaps they might have questioned it, but given the set of circumstances, they held me in their arms and offered all of their support. They didn't really like it but recognized that it was for the best.Together we went through the files. Dad made comparative charts and we studied each testimony in detail. Several weeks of work and meditation went into our decision.

When we sent the name of the couple that we had chosen, I felt that I had taken the most difficult step in my life.

The director called my house and told me how happy the couple that I had selected was. Half an hour later, he called again to ask me for some more information and added that the parents-to-be were still crying, overcome with joy.

To know that my baby was so wanted gave me some peace, but as the date for the delivery approached, my emotions became gloomy and melancholic. At moments I regretted my decision and wanted to take it back; it was like being on a roller coaster moving up to take the first dip but realizing too late that what I really wanted was to get off.

During those months I matured a lot; becoming a woman, learning to rely on God, the Supreme Entity that the twelve steps talked about...

It was a natural delivery. I suffered agonizing pains that were perhaps even stronger because they were accompanied by a great sadness. After I gave birth, hearing the baby cry, I pleaded:

"Let me see him."

"We're sorry," answered a voice, "but you can't. The adoption regulations forbid it."

"I need to say good-bye to him," I cried, "please."

"It's not possible, we're sorry."

I heard them walk away.

"Stop!" I screamed. "Don't go. The adoption is a bitter pill I'm taking to save him and I'm going to take it. I promise you, just let me give him my blessing. Please! That's all I ask."

There was silence in the room. The physicians knew that they shouldn't risk violating the rules, but neither could they deny me what I requested.

"Only one minute..." they said.

They put a baby boy on my chest.

I cried as I embraced him, caressing him, covering him with kisses, speaking to him softly as I explained what would happen. He was quiet, as if he understood me. My tears wet his face. I expressed all the love in my heart for him and declared that for that reason, and only for that reason, I could allow him to be separated from me.

I know that the blessing of a mother always accompanies her child and that it is a Grace prophecy. I blessed my baby with all my heart... When the physician approached to take him, I closed my eyes and I truly felt I was giving him to God. I knew that He took him in His arms and promised me that He would look after him and be by his side always.

Perhaps if I hadn't had that absolute conviction, years later, I might have gone crazy seeking the son that I gave up... At any rate I've suffered a lot but without despairing, invested with the peace of mind that I did the best thing for him. From this extremely painful experience, I've gained a tremendous insight: that no one has the right or can destroy a living creature, regardless of the suffering endured. Each person is a unique, extraordinary and very valuable human being. The surprising results of surviving a tragedy like this is that by living through it you're led to a higher level of personal growth. The more unexplainable the pain may seem to the human mind, the more power of enrichment there is behind it, and the longer it will be remembered leaving its footprints, supporting in the end a greater good. Many who suffer will never understand, therefore, they shouldn't despair. Spiritual faith moves mountains.

To accept her past, her physical appearance and to regard herself as a human being loved by the Creator, with great value and with a mission to fulfill was... perhaps... what Alma lacked...

I held Lisbeth's hand and squeezed it firmly.

"Thanks." I said to her while wiping away my tears with my free hand.

"Zahid, tell me something," she asked me, "when we called the hospital, they didn't want to give us any information, but you were angry and demanded that they tell you what kind of hospital it was. You turned pale when they answered, but you didn't tell me what they said... Where are we going? Where did your sister write from? Why did she ask you in her letter: '*If you can't come to see me, please, don't tell anyone where I am.*"

I looked down without answering her question. Lisbeth tried guessing.

"It's a psychiatric hospital, right?"

I shook my head.

"Then...?"

A chill traveled down my spine when I said it.

"It's a hospital for drug addicts."

We arrived at our destination and immediately got out of the taxi. I gave the driver the paid ticket from the airport and walked with the weight of the world on my shoulders towards the hospital's entrance. Suddenly I recalled Lisbeth's words before making the trip:

"Zahid, I've just noticed something else that you're not going to like... Your sister wrote this letter a month ago. She didn't date it, but the stamp shows it."

I turned around and yelled for the taxi to stop as it was already leaving. I caught up to it, feeling a bit out of breath.

"We're looking for a person that was hospitalized," I explained, "but it's very possible that she might not be here anymore and we may have to go to another place. Could you wait and take us if necessary?"

"Of course." The driver answered, not being able to conceal the happiness of collecting some extra cash in the wee hours of the morning.

He backed up and parked the car.

When I entered the hospital, my wife was already speaking with a nun that seemed to be in charge of the front desk.

She was explaining, "It's very urgent that we know about Alma Duarte. She's one of your patients. We received a letter from her and we've just made a very long trip to come and see her."

"Duarte, you said, right?"

We nodded while she opened the filing cabinet and looked carefully. After a while, which seemed to take forever, she straightened up and said, as she closed the drawer:

"There isn't a file under that name, are you sure she was in this hospital?"

"We're sure."

"There couldn't be a mistake?"

I felt irritated. I took out my wallet and looked for the wrinkled card in which I wrote down the address that they had given me over the telephone and threw it on the counter.

"I called yesterday, at about six o'clock in the evening, I asked about my sister and was informed that she was your patient, but that they couldn't give me any information over the phone. That's why we're here."

"Who did you talk to?"

"Miss, I don't know, but I can tell you that she was not a courteous person. I hope that you're different."

"Alma Duarte, is that right?"

"Yes."

The nun walked toward a private office and went in. After some minutes she came out, accompanied by a plump woman dressed in white. Both of them seemed a little disturbed.

"Are you Alma's family?"

"Yes!" I almost screamed. "She's my sister."

"What do you know about her?" she asked.

"What should we know? She lived with my parents several years ago, but decided to be independent, that's all."

The woman watched me as if she were waiting for me to say more.

"She is in fact our patient... But... It's a special case."

"Special?"

"Yes. You don't know what's happened to her during the last years?"

I shook my head, feeling the premonition of something evil begin to haunt me.

"Well, given the circumstances," the nurse concluded with the cautious weariness of a jailer, "I can't give you any information about this patient. You'll have to wait for the social psychologist. If I call her right now, she can be here in a couple of hours."

"But how dare you... you must tell me!" I almost jumped on the counter, prisoner of an uncontrollable rage. The two frightened women stepped back.

14

The Skyscraper

In the austere reception area of the hospital, Lisbeth and I found ourselves leaning against each other, anticipating the arrival of the social psychologist.

I could have forced the nurses to give me the information that they were keeping from me, but they locked themselves in the office and didn't come out until they thought that I had calmed down.

"Besides," I rationalized, "it's a very inappropriate hour to visit Alma, wherever she is."

The taxi driver furiously stomped in demanding to know if we were going to need his services. I stood up to apologize and gave him a generous tip from my wallet as payment for his waiting. The man grabbed it and left without thanking me.

I sat down again next to my wife and closed my eyes trying to calm down. In order to distract my mind, I ran through various topics: *the upcoming inauguration ceremony for my company, the strange trip that we had just made, the way in which Lisbeth and I had met again.*

Unwillingly, my thoughts stopped there.

She was thirty two; I was thirty three. Lisbeth had been granted an award for her work as director of the "Center for the Protection of Women". She was a psychologist with postgraduate studies related to the motivation of human behaviour. I was part of the committee that granted the awards and was sitting at the head table when the master of ceremonies called Lisbeth. The public applauded. A slim elegant woman walked up to the stage to receive her award. As soon as she came near, I was sure I had seen her before and knew who she was. Even though my memory was delayed, my heart reacted immediately, it jumped and began to beat as if it were in front of the woman that I had dreamed about for years, waiting patiently for the hour in which I could see her again: Is it her? I questioned my incredulous mind. No. It can't be... It's been too long... I personally gave her the certificate and congratulated her with a hand shake. Then she went to the podium and gave a short speech of grateful acceptance. Her way of leaning towards the microphone, her way of looking at the audience, with tenderness and authority, her clear and poised voice, her sincerity and magnetism, left me no doubt. I had spent so many years thinking and daydreaming about what I'd say to the young woman with the unforgettable testimony if I ever met her again... My hands trembled contemplating her.

The audience applauded. Lisbeth descended from the podium just as I excused myself and discreetly went through the other door of the stage.

The conference about "values" was coming to an end. As the director of the National Association of Young Entrepreneurs, I had been assigned the closing speech and only had three or four minutes before my discourse. I hurriedly told one of the ushers to locate the previous speaker and ask her to come and see me.

"Do you remember me?" I asked her bluntly, as soon as she arrived accompanied by the usher.

"No." she answered with a puzzled expression.

"I remember your testimony about how you were molested and felt disgraced."

She blushed immediately and felt a little frightened as she watched me.

"It was on that occasion at your support group, when you gave a speech about 'how to love life' that you really shocked me, motivating me to make a drastic change. You spoke about the bird that lived resigned in a rotten tree in the middle of the swamp, eating worms, dirty by the stagnated mud, until one day a great gust of wind destroyed his shelter and he was forced to fly away, arriving finally at a fertile forest. The figure of the bird flying over the quicksand has motivated me for many years to get out of my own mire."

Lisbeth made an effort to recall. She studied me with her eyes.

"Back then," I helped her, "I didn't have this glass eye... I was a shy kid... Reading and highlighting a book in the lobby of the conference hall for support groups."

She observed me for a few seconds without being able to articulate a word.

"My God," she finally uttered. "What a small world."

The master of ceremonies announced the closing speech.

"I have to say a few words," I excused myself. "Please, don't go. There are so many things I'd like to share with you."

I went up on stage and began my speech by saying how happy I was because today I had just met the woman that years ago motivated me, without knowing it, to achieve my highest goals.

You can achieve your dreams, above all if you fight for love. Love for God, for yourselves, for the life that you have, for the mate that perhaps you don't know yet.

Thinking about that special person, one day I decided to fight with all I had. She deserved my greatest effort and I had to improve so that when the right moment came along, I'd be able to give her my best.

One night I went to bed wondering what the key to success really was.

Then I dreamt that life was a huge skyscraper where we had to rise to the top.

All human beings began to rise from one of many floors depending on the socioeconomic level in which they were born, but even the most privileged found themselves on lower floors since the skyscraper was infinitely high.

On each floor there were two perfectly differentiated zones:

***FIRST. THE ROOM OF DISTRACTIONS:** A huge room, filled with friends, beds, televisions, parties and games, in which you could have an extraordinary time for many years.*

***SECOND. THE TUNNEL OF ELEVATORS:** A long wide cor-*

ridor full of workshops and study tables in which you could acquire knowledge and experience.

This huge hallway was called "the tunnel of elevators", because its walls were covered with elevator doors. When the doors of an elevator opened, many people jumped up and ran towards it. Quickly, a line was formed. The elevator operator then asked a question to the first person in line. If he didn't know the answer, he was disqualified, continuing to the next person in line, and thus until he reached the person who had the required knowledge to answer correctly; this person was allowed to get on the elevator and was transported to a higher floor; meanwhile, the door of the elevator closed to the sad looks of all the rejected faces... Some, disappointed, went to the distractions room, others remained in the tunnel to try again.

There were some who spent their time walking and waiting for an elevator to open, but without working or studying, so they never rose because they didn't have the required knowledge.

Others, on the contrary, spent their time working but didn't get up from their seats when the elevator opened. These, though they had the knowledge, were too shy to be chosen.

The person that managed to rise found, on the new floor, an even more attractive room of distractions than the lower floors. In the same way the tunnel of elevators had workshops and study tables of much greater difficulty; therefore, the higher the floor, the less candidates there were to rise each time an elevator door opened.

An interesting detail caught my attention: those who remained downstairs cowardly criticized and put down those who managed to rise higher. They attacked them excusing their rise simply to luck. And in my dream I knew that if luck meant to have the necessary knowledge and at the same time to have the agility to stand in front of the door that opened then, in fact, great men were very lucky.

I paused to observe the audience.

Pleasantly surprised, I verified that Lisbeth was listening to me. She was still standing where I had left her. I felt thrilled and continued my speech with greater energy and confidence:

If you have a wealthy relative, don't think you have the right to ask him for money. If he refuses to help you don't accuse him of being stingy, greedy, miserly, tight or selfish. Perhaps he acquired what he has because he's lost less time than you in the room of distractions or because while you keep making plans without moving a finger, he has painstakingly prepared himself in the tunnel of elevators and has been watching and ready to move when the doors open. That's it, very simply.

You can rise as high as you want. Only those with minds behind the times ask for a handout; consequently, they become useless even though they may be only twenty years old... But if you are young at heart... You can achieve your dreams.

It's good to ask God for what you want. It's all right to speak to Him and to confide in Him about your dreams, but instead of saying: "God, help me in my business, the interview or the exam that I'm going to do," today, I challenge you to change how you ask Him and make your prayer petition a statement of faith: "Lord, what I have to do today, I'll do the very best I can, I'll make my greatest effort enthusiastically. Watch me in the interview or in the exam. I offer you all I have and leave the results in your hands and by your will..."

That's how to be responsible.

There's a story about a man who forgot his bicycle at the market. The following day, disappointed, sure of the fact that someone had taken it, returned to look for it. He was filled with joy upon finding it exactly where he had left it. When he was on his way back to his house he went by a church, he stopped to thank God for having looked after his bicycle all night, and when he left the church, his bicycle was gone...

My friends. God does not look after bicycles. He gives you warnings so that you do your part... You have the intelligence, the will, the conscience, the body; all the elements to succeed. If you don't achieve your dreams it's because you didn't pay the price. Period. That's it... Don't beat around the bushes, don't make any more excuses... Start doing what you have to do, today. I challenge you to turn your best effort into your best prayer...

Don't forget: Two basic elements are required in order to rise through the skyscraper. ***PREPARATION AND A SENSE OF URGENCY.***

Get moving, be attentive to the doors that open, know that your time is important, don't let this day go by without having used it properly. There are people who act like they haven't any life, they seem to have oil in their veins, when they're at work they spend their time watching the hands of the clock and counting the minutes to leave. Parasites!, scum of the earth!, critics that envy the success of others!, mediocre people who tear apart those who are higher up!, those with small minds who spitefully can't stand to see others get ahead and succeed, and much less if they live nearby or are in the same city or country; or are the same age or younger...! But understand this... It only takes two elements in order to rise: ***A SENSE OF URGENCY AND PREPARATION.*** *Pay the price to be somebody...! Be ready to move in the corridor of elevators!*

Invest in your mind... Learn, prepare yourself... Your value has nothing to do with the monetary worth of your assets; you're worth what you have in your mind... Increase your mental capacity and the rest will come along... Solely what you store in your intellect is what will take you directly towards your dreams...

A little while ago I listened to a lady, who was complaining about her maid by saying:

"The poor girl, she's illiterate..."

Years after, I learned that there wasn't much difference between the two of them, since her housekeeper didn't know how to read and yet the lady ***knew how but didn't bother to,*** *so actually they were equals. One DID NOT have the ability, the other had it, but didn't use it... That's called: "being an illiterate with credentials."*

Understand this once and for all... You'll never rise to the top of the skyscraper without paying the price of filling your mind with concepts and looking for open doors with courage and decision. It's as simple as that. There's no room on the top floors for those who waste their time at parties, watch television obsessively, spend hours on the telephone, go out to kill time, seek any kind of distractions, watch movie after movie, rest and sleep all the time...

One more piece of advice: ORGANIZE YOURSELF... Don't act like a wind up doll. Your ***clear focus to direct*** *your sense of urgency is indispensable to achieve the results that you desire. Don't waste your energies on trivial matters. Put your priorities in order. There are lots of people that spend hours running from one place to another, but nothing of what they do is indeed valuable. They believe that the busier they are, the more important they are... and frequently they complain about feeling exhausted and nervous, but what produces more tension, is to know that they have been postponing their important projects by occupying themselves in irrelevant matters. There are two kinds of human beings: flea hunters and elephant hunters. If you waste time in a thousand unimportant details you'll end up exhausted and you'll only have some tiny fleas in your bag. If on the contrary, you concentrate on transcendental matters, perhaps you'll work the same amount, but you'll trap pachyderms.* ***What matters is not how busy you are, but how much of what you're doing is really important...***

Do what needs to be done! Stop sighing and acting like a martyr! If you don't succeed, it's because you don't feel like it! Don't make another excuse, since there isn't one. GO TO THE FRONT LINE... Make yourself heard, make yourself valuable... "Work and promote yourself." If you don't believe in yourself, no one else will. If you don't raise your hand for fear of being criticized, you might as well die because nobody will miss you. Struggle! Even a striving poet is better that an isolated poet! The man who calls himself intellectual or spiritual and then withdraws permanently from reality, is in fact, a procastinator. When you're dead, you can commune with the spirits whenever you want, however, today, your country, your company and your family need ***KNOWLEDGE AND ACTION****. Procastination is a synonym of cowardice. To face the world with courage is the only way to arrive first at the elevator and to make history. You will never reach your goals if you sit in the room of distractions, eating popcorn, watching a movie and complaining about your bad luck...!*

When I finished the speech I was sweating and my hair was all messed up. I slid behind the curtain to go to one of the dressing rooms.

I was wiping my forehead and drinking a little bit of water when Lisbeth showed up.

The door was open, she entered without knocking and walked up to me silently. She seemed nervous, and yet exceptionally beautiful... I didn't know what to do or what to say.

The love that has greater possibilities of lasting is NOT forged in moments of immaturity. Both of us had learnt ALONE how to pay the price of rising inside the skyscraper. After fifteen years we had met again!

Neither one of us attempted to say a word. It was one of the most beautiful moments of my life.

"What I said at the beginning," I finally told her, "about the woman that motivated me to improve myself yet without her knowing it... was you."

"I understood that. I only came to thank you."

Then I dared myself to take a step towards her. I put a hand on her arm and in an affectionate gesture I said to her that I admired and respected her very much and that, if she would accept, I'd like to invite her to dinner.

Startled by the sudden opening of the hospital's door, I came back to reality.

"Did you fall asleep?" asked Lisbeth.

"No. I was just remembering with my eyes closed."

A tall woman with abundant red hair entered the lobby, greeted us courteously and continued towards the offices.

We hoped that she was the social psychologist that we had been waiting for. We weren't mistaken.

After a few minutes, the nun came out and invited us to go in.

The room was extremely small. There was only an old metallic desk and two vinyl covered chairs. We sat in front of the woman who had put on a white smock. The receptionist left the room closing the door behind her. Either it was a very warm morning or I was indeed exasperated, because I felt that I was suffocating.

"Are you relatives of Alma Duarte?"

"She's my sister."

The woman leafed through the file that was in front of her. Her attitude was confusing.

"They called me in to speak with you. It's three o'clock in the morning. You must understand that there are few emergencies for a social psychologist."

Lisbeth and I remained silent, waiting for the woman to stop beating around the bushes.

"What was the last thing that you knew about your sister?"

I felt irritated.

"She left the family at seventeen and went to live with a guy who was triple her age and a real tyrant. I wrote to her every month but she never answered my letters. I also sent her hundreds of books and cassettes. She is a very beautiful woman, but has suffered some... traumas. Do you need to know more?"

"And why are you looking for her here?"

I took the letter out of my pocket and gave it to her. She unfolded it and read it quickly. After putting it down on the table, she began to speak slowly, carefully choosing her words.

"As a matter of fact, Alma was in this hospital over a month ago. They brought her here unconscious because of a drug overdose."

"Is she alive?"

The time that the woman delayed in answering me were the longest seconds than I can ever remember.

"She is a heroin addict..."

I nodded slowly, feeling the impact of the news, though I already expected to hear something like that. However, there had to be more. It didn't make sense that in a hospital of this sort, there was so much protocol in order to give us the information that was so evident from the beginning.

"But, is she all right?" asked Lisbeth.

"When she was more than halfway through the treatment, she ran away."

"And, do you know where she is?"

She looked down, as if it was something very sad.

"I'm afraid so."

She took the letter in her hands again.

"I've visited her a couple of times, but she doesn't want to talk to me... Mr. Duarte, have you realized the depth of the letter that she wrote to you?"

I felt like a child reprimanded by his mother... The woman seemed to be trying to tell us something that we should have already known.

"Here it says: *'Zahid, I have lost, just like you, something irreplaceable... Do you know? The truth is I wish I wasn't a woman; I wish I wasn't so weak; I wish I hadn't buried myself in my own misery; I wish I had never been born...'.*"

I stood up with my hand on my forehead and raised my voice, exasperated.

"Miss, could you please, stop talking in circles and get to the point? Where is my sister?"

The woman took a piece of paper and wrote down an address. Then she handed it to me. I read it, but it didn't give me a clue.

"You can find her there."

"What is this?"

"The address to her apartment."

I opened the door of the tiny room ready to get out. That was all I needed. I tugged at Lisbeth's arm so that she would hurry and we could leave. The psychologist stopped me.

"I recommend that you don't go at this time. It's three o'clock in the morning and..."

"And what...?" I screamed with my eyes popping out of their sockets. "Once and for all, speak clearly. My sister is an adult woman. If she has another lover, why are you making this so complicated?"

"No, Mr. Duarte," and then, dragging the words out of her mouth one by one, she said to me: "She is a prostitute..."

15

Why did you exclude me?

A waterfall of freezing water seemed to spew out all over my head.

I took a step forward and let myself fall on the chair feeling the blood in my veins become paralyzed.

"We tried to help her here," explained the woman, "but things got complicated."

She took a pencil and began to turn it around very slowly.

"She's immersed in circumstances which are not easy to get out of... After the diagnosis she fell into a terrible depression. She continued to inject herself with drugs. She needs help. Urgently. It's good you came... The family can be of great help in these cases, but when I spoke with her in this regard she assured me that she had no family."

For the first time in many years, I felt that I was falling apart.

Most of us men believe that the women at home have insensitive and useless porcelain bodies. Therefore, we never speak about sex with them and sometimes the deception turns into anger when we find out, not always under pleasant circumstances, that the little sister or daughter also practices her sexuality. That happened to me when Alma left with that guy. Today, the stake went in even deeper. I had achieved a good financial position. I always did everything I could to help my sister. She was selling her body in order to live? Why didn't she accept the help that I so insistently offered? Was it possible she didn't do it for money but because of a total and absolute degradation? Was she practicing the oldest trade of all in order to get drugs for herself? Or did the drugs come after? Why did she write to me asking for help if she was already in so deep? Why didn't she react before?

I covered my face with both hands.

Lisbeth hugged me from behind and wanted to give me hope, but my pain transferred to her so much that she was speechless.

After an undefinable time, we got up with a certain clumsiness, as if we had recently suffered an accident. In a way we had. The vehicle in which my soul traveled had gone down a cliff and I was trying to get out of the remains, not believing what had happened to me, or that I was still alive.

The psychologist asked us if she could go with us to see my sister.

"No," I answered her. "It's not necessary... She must face the fact that she does have a family. Perhaps she needs to tell me some very serious things and I don't want any witnesses when that happens."

We went to the front desk of the hospital and I asked the nun to please call a taxi. She obeyed immediately without asking any questions. She respected other people's pain and realized, by looking at us, that we already knew what she could not or did not want to tell us.

The car arrived almost immediately.

We gave the driver the address and he drove to the place in complete silence. During the drive, Lisbeth held my hand tight. I was buried in my thoughts, trying to disentangle the cobweb.

We arrived at Alma's apartment and I was surprised to discover it was in a well to do area, with wide avenues and luxurious restaurants.

I looked at my watch. It was going to be four o'clock in the morning.

I moved my head in confusion:

"Perhaps, like the psychologist said, it would be embarrassing to burst into her intimacy at this hour."

The taxi driver turned completely around to look at us.

"Should I take you somewhere else?"

"Yes," I answered, "to the nearest hotel." I turned to look at Lisbeth, "We can get some sleep for a couple of hours before beginning our search. I have the feeling it's going to be a very hard day."

"All right," she approved, comforted by seeing me calmed.

"Five blocks away," said the driver, "there's a hotel. It's nearby but not exactly for tourists."

"Go ahead," I approved. "Any place is good simply to sleep for a while."

Lisbeth objected: "As long as it's clean."

"It is. It's good and expensive."

We went directly to the place and got out of the taxi.

We realized that in fact, the hotel was luxurious, but designed especially for the continuous traffic of furtive couples. A painful idea crossed my mind. Certainly my sister didn't use her private apartment to "work"; I sharpened my sight, fearful, thinking that she might be around.

"How funny," said Lisbeth, as if trying to lighten up the moment, "did you notice the number of cars that there are in this place?"

"Yes." I answered, following her little game of covering the deep sorrow that took us there. "A friend of mine, a businessman, told me that tourist hotels have serious problems keeping solvent, but those for 'prostitution' are commonly found at full capacity."

"And what does that indicate?"

"The incredible amount of infidelities that take place. Young couples can't afford what it costs to come frequently to a place like this, therefore, the majority of those who use them are adults. In general they're married people, and a married man, most of the time, does not bring his wife to one of these hotels... I bet you that most of the rooms around us are occupied by people that are cheating on their spouses."

We entered the foyer and requested a room. The young man at the counter had problems finding a vacancy. Finally, after changing his mind twice, he gave us the key and indicated the way. He didn't even ask us if we had any luggage. It was obvious that we didn't.

We got to the room and went in.

In fact, it was pleasant and clean. It seemed like a love nest, although there was something that felt artificial in the environment.

I sat on the bed and took off my shoes. Lisbeth sat near me. I embraced her feeling again the overpowering weight of disbelief.

This was too incredible to be conceived, too overwhelming to be understood. I looked at her through a haze.

"Why?"

She shrugged her shoulders, silently saying to me: *"I don't know why this happened, believe me; and I have no idea what we're going to do, but I'm at your side; cry with me if you want to."*

I regained my self-control and decidedly took the telephone.

"Who are you calling?" she asked.

"My parents. They live around here. Even though Alma doesn't want any one to know where she is, they have the right..."

"Calm down. Relax...I'll make the call. In a while. For now, get some rest..."

She took the receiver from my hand and pushed me back very gently. I embraced her warm body and, without knowing how or when, fell soundly asleep.

I didn't dream anything. My body was so exhausted and my mind so shocked that I literally traveled to another dimension for four hours.

In my lethargy I heard, in the distance, the water from the shower.

When I awoke, it took me a few seconds to realize where I was and to recall the sea of troubles confronting me. Contrary to other times, abandoning my placid dreams rudely shoved me into the nightmare of my reality. It was past eight in the morning and Lisbeth was finishing her shower.

Leaving the bathroom, she informed me that my parents were already on their way.

I combed my hair and straightened my wrinkled shirt. Lisbeth was almost ready when we heard them knock.

I opened the door, shaking with a certain uneasiness.

My mother, a little heavier than she was at my wedding, four months ago, was examining me behind my dad.

"Come in."

"Thanks. Your wife called us."
"Yes. Come in."
My parents greeted their daughter-in-law with a kiss and turned towards me, visibly concerned.
"Is it true that you've found Alma? How is she?"
"Today you'll be updated on the depressing news," I said slowly.
"What's happening?"
"Something serious."
My mother was the first to guess.
"Has she become an alcoholic?"
"Why do you ask? Do you know something about her... addictions?"
"No. I mean... what addictions?"
"We made this pressing trip because Alma wrote me a letter from a hospital."
"Did she have an accident?"
"In a way. Heroine addicts never know if the dose that they're injecting themselves with is correct..."
"Alma is..."
"Yes." I confirmed. "Furthermore, she's a prostitute."
My father almost fell over. Mother, on the contrary, opened her eyes wide and threw herself at me, hysterically hitting me with her fists.
"You're lying! Liar! You're saying that just to get back at us! It's a lie! Right? Say it's a lie..."
Still beating me, although with less intensity each time, she slowly slipped down to the floor. I intervened and led her to the bed so that she could sit down. I was not moved by her scene. It was impossible to define how legitimate it was.
"I'm going to ask you something and I want you to tell me the truth." I glared at dad with my good eye, sure that it would be enough for him to realize how frustrated I was. "What the devil happened to her *before* she ran away with that man?"

For some seconds neither one of the two dared to speak.

My mother kept on crying.

Without looking at him, she said:

"We're going to have to tell him."

Lisbeth was standing near the wall without being able to assimilate the profundity of what she was witnessing. The air turned so dense that it was difficult to breath. A dark shadow fell over the room, the shadow of a matter that they knew all about but had possibly tried to forget.

"Did you lose your speech, Dad?"

"No," he answered in a falsetto voice, "when we found out... we decided to move."

"When you found out *what*?"

I tried putting the information together. They moved out of the apartment building when I was in my last year of college. What could have happened at that time, serious enough to make them move, so extremely serious that it was kept in absolute secrecy?

"When I was an active alcoholic," began Dad, "you fractured your arm because I pushed you down the staircase..." he stopped to find the best way to say it. "Alma was nine and you were fifteen. While your mother rushed you to the hospital, Ro came down from his apartment and helped me get into the house and lay down. Alma was crying, very upset. When I fell asleep, Ro took her to the living room explaining that she didn't need to be afraid, that he'd always take care of her and protect her."

What was he talking about? I covered my face with both hands trying to understand what was behind his words.

"Have you ever felt that you're useless?"

"What are you talking about?"

"I don't know... But sometimes I feel like that. Stupid, not wanting to live... This world is a bunch of crap... I spend too much time alone... Uncle Ro is the only one who understands me... I'm just depressed."

Had she said: *Only my Uncle Ro?*

A sharp knife carved its way right through my brain when the truth began to sink in...

"Your pain was known by all and that helped you heal, mine on the other hand, was secret and it's been killing me slowly throughout the years..."

My God, it couldn't be true...

Cold shivers turned my skin into goose flesh and I felt that my heart was breaking in two...

"Alma was very scared of Ro," said my mother finally, "but at the same time she felt flattered that he considered her someone special. It wasn't until very late in her adolescence that she realized what he had been doing to her was called incest..."

Hearing the last word, the horror hit me like an electric shock, leaving me paralyzed.

Had I heard right?

Like a person with heart problems that has done more exercise than he should, I leaned against the wall, putting my hand on my chest feeling that I was about to faint.

"You were at college," Dad added, taking the reins of the conversation, "one day she arrived home drunk. I was frightened believing she might fall into the same trap I was escaping. I reprimanded her very severely. Then she said to me that she had already gotten drunk before, with her uncle. I shook her and demanded that she finish explaining everything to me. She had to be drunk to reveal to us what my brother had done to her... The impact and my guilt were so severe that I started drinking again. I relapsed in the worst way. I became much more dependent than before. I was on the verge of dying..."

My mother had stopped crying and was sitting on the edge of the bed with her eyes staring straight ahead. It seemed that her memory had begun to drift into the dark past and that she had lost the capacity to evaluate the consequences of what she was recalling.

My father started talking again in his low monotonous voice:

"Alma confessed to us that Ro seemed to have a special sixth sense to guess when she was available. He would lock the door and then teach her all sorts of kisses and hugs, touch her under her clothes and would force her to... to touch his 'private parts'. Sometimes she felt disgusted and cried, but he repeatedly said he didn't want to hurt her, that he was very sad and alone since he lost his wife and that she really was the most important person in his life. If we arrived unexpectedly, he would disappear by going up the winding staircase."

"Wait a moment," I interrupted him, feeling my blood begin to boil in my veins. "Ro did this to a *nine* year old girl?"

They didn't answer. The response was affirmative.

"Mother," I said, attacking her, "what did you do? Didn't you help her?"

She shook her head bursting again into terrible sobs.

"No one suspected what was going on. Your sister was awfully quiet."

"But she helped Ro to arrange the movie cases at the video store every night! You asked her to do it in order to pay back all that pig had supposedly done for us. Why weren't you more careful? She was just a child!"

There was no response.

Much later I learned that behind the counter, while Alma arranged the cases, he would touch her; until one night he tried to penetrate her but couldn't completely and left her hurt and bleeding. Justifying himself, he told her that it was something natural and that she had to learn to be a woman. He insisted that her mother and father did the same thing and that all men and women did it... Alma's body closed itself to all possible penetration and the degenerated man resigned himself to ejaculate by forcing the girl to touch him and kiss him.

My mother cried, broken beyond words. She couldn't or didn't want to speak. I was a prisoner of an enormous rage, indescribable, worse than any I'd felt in my entire life.

"You moved when Alma was seventeen," I calculated. "Why didn't you ever say anything to me...?"

"We didn't want to worry you," explained Dad. "You were finishing your degree with honors and wanted to start postgraduate studies."

"But why...!" I screamed, punching the wooden chest very hard. "What right did you have to hide from me what had happened to my sister?"

"We didn't think that you would take it like this."

Furiously sobbing, I'd never felt so powerless, so sadly frustrated and so humiliated for having been excluded.

It's incredible how many things can happen near us without us even knowing! Parents tend to be the last to find out about their children's sexual problems; spouses that are cheated on are the last to know about their partner's affair; siblings are the last to learn about their mutual heartbreaks...

Lisbeth, astounded, stiff, stared at the floor. Certainly she had listened to many similar testimonies, but this paralyzed her because of the way it personally affected us. I had squeezed my fists with such force that my knuckles turned white. I recalled the expression on my little sister's face at the hospital, while looking after me. Always so helpful and sweet... At that time, I couldn't have imagined that the same innocent child had lived more than I had. She knew the evilness of the world more intrinsically and had been trapped in a more wounding and abusive situation than mine.

"Dad," I said to him, furiously. "To become rehabilitated from an illness like yours implies a tremendous spiritual growth, and it also implies being surrounded by positive people. Why didn't you transmit all of what you knew to your daughter?"

"There wasn't any time, do you understand? *Time* was the problem... When she revealed everything to us, I had the relapse. I went back to the rehabilitation clinic. I was in treatment for several months. When I recovered, we moved and I began to try and help her, but she had become callused hard and emotionally closed. A few weeks after, she ran away with that jerk..."

"And I," said my mother finally with an intermittent voice, "consoled her, I tried to take her to a psychologist, but she wouldn't accept anything from me. She hated me."

"What did you do to Ro?"

"As soon as we heard, I went upstairs to vent my anger and yell at him; we got into a fist fight," said Dad. "Your grandmother watched the scene. It seems that she never recovered from that. After that she was diagnosed with the diabetes."

"Poor thing!" I mocked. "What else did you do?"

"He was family, we couldn't have him thrown in jail. Your grandmother's health was at stake. We moved away from him. That was all."

"I can't believe it..."

"Dear," interrupted Lisbeth as she approached me, "it's getting late. We should go to see Alma right now."

16

Abuse to minors

We threw our key into the hotel checkout box and walked towards the exit without saying a word.

Dad had parked his car across the street.

Lisbeth and I got into the back seat. I almost sat on a huge Bible marked with various annotations.

"What a surprise," I said to my father, "do you read this BOOK?"

"I'm preparing a devotional. On Sunday it's my turn to say a few words at church."

A certain excitement, full of approval, invaded me. Something good must have happened to my father after so much time, but suddenly I realized something wasn't right and I asked:

"Are you 'painting monsters'?"

"Don't make fun of me."

"Of course not. You know that I'm a firm believer, but when I see someone who's unable to turn his theological concepts into their everyday way of life, then I believe that he is a 'painter of monsters'."

"Painting what...?"

"Yes. The artist who paints dogs, cats or horses has to be a professional because *everyone knows* what those animals look like. However, the person who paints monsters can draw frightful creatures any way he wants and they'll always turn out right."

He observed me without understanding. I continued motivated by a fire that hadn't been put out:

"To take the Bible and use it declaring that *"God doesn't like your attitude"*, *"God will get angry for what you think"*, *"God is sad"*, *"God told me that you should do that"*, is painting monsters. You know that you won't fail because no one has ever seen God, because you're hiding behind a mask pretending to represent an authority using His name when you don't even know Him. **TO SAY** something is one thing, is that clear? Because **TO DO** things is quite different, it's like painting human faces. Everyone will know if you make a mistake."

"I'm sorry, but I don't have any idea of what you're talking about."

"It doesn't matter. We never did understand each other."

We arrived at Alma's apartment.

We knocked at the door and waited, but no one opened it.

I tried to look inside through the thick curtain while Lisbeth knocked again. It was useless. There was no one there. I felt helpless, not knowing what to do next. Should we wait? For how long? Hours? Days?

I felt desperate.

"Alma!" I screamed, hitting the glass with the palm of my hand. "It's Zahid. If you're there, open up...!"

The next-door neighbor opened her door and looked at us threateningly.

"Do you know the person that lives here?" I asked her, feeling embarrassed for all the noise.

"I'm not friends with her."

"But, do you know where she could be?"

"No."

The neighbor closed her door with spite. Frustrated beyond belief, I clenched my fists while I kicked Alma's door.

We looked at each other without knowing what to do.

"We know her former address," Dad said, "it's a little far, but perhaps they might be able to tell us something about her."

"And if she returns here?" I objected.

"Zahid and I can wait here while you two go."

They nodded and left without saying good-bye. We watched them leave.

I really didn't want to stay and "just wait" there. Due to my hyperactive nature, it was a sacrifice for me to stand still.

Lisbeth and I put our arms around each other and leaned against the railing, looking down, in an atmosphere of deep foreboding grief.

"What happened to your sister," she said almost whispering, "is more common than you think."

I studied her, feeling confused and trying to make some sense out of it all. I grasped onto the idea of conversing *not* with my wife but with the director of the *Center for the Protection of Women.*

"Everybody knows that these things happen," I uttered, "but, to what degree?"

"To the degree that anyone can have a case like Alma's in their family."

Tormented, I listened to every word she said, sheltering the hope that I'd hear something to relieve the crushing weight asphixiating me. She noticed my eagerness and began speaking very carefully:

"Around us there are thousands of incest cases every day. **The victims vary from two months to eighteen years of age."** She stopped to contemplate me with tenderness. I nodded to her so that she would continue. "Of the million young people that run away from their home every year," she detailed, "it's been proven that forty to sixty percent *do it because they've suffered sexual abuse."*[1]

I glared at the door to my sister's apartment.

"And why didn't she run away? Why didn't she try to rebuild her life? Why did the consequences of this problem follow her until it reached these extremes measures?"

"Your sister is not in this situation by chance. Whether the coital act was completed or not, the damage of incest is almost never physical, it's psychological. It produces ***a lack of confidence, obsessive fears, shyness, low self-esteem, shame, a deep sensation of guilt and the inability to say 'no' to subsequent sexual pressures, isolation and depression..."***

---

[1] Kempe and Kempe, (Sexual Abuse of Children and Adolescents. New York. W.H. Freeman and Co. 1984) referred to in: *Earl Wilson, "A Silence to be Broken". Hope for the victims of incest. Vida Editorial.*

I picked a leaf from an artificial plant that adorned the terrace and admired how real it appeared. Anyone would have said that Alma and I were friends. Human bonds of friendship are many times exactly like that, beautiful on the outside, but on the inside artificial, plastic and superficial, just like the leaves on the plant.

"I thought that these things only happened in fiction." I murmured, as if talking to myself.

"Well, Zahid. You and I have watched movies that show a woman selling her body on the street because of the severe trauma that incest produced in her... But, sadly enough, this situation is very common and as old as history. You must realize that the sexual abuse of girls is the reason for the great majority of prostitution. The results of a recent survey show that eighty percent of the prostitutes suffered sexual abuse during their childhood, that eighty percent of those who rape minors were raped *when they were children*, and that most of the women that have suffered abuse *in their childhood*, develop sexual dysfunctions when they grow up.[2] Besides this, there's child pornography, magazines and movies that openly promote incest and rape."[3]

I remained speechless for a long while, astonished by the terrible data that the founder of the *Center for the Protection of Women* was giving me.

"What a world we live in..." I sighed heavily.

"Abuse to minors is a serious problem."

"But how do you stop it?" I asked.

"To start, **by teaching children from a very young age that their opinion is important; that everything they feel is valid and deserves to be acknowledged, that they have the right to disagree, to say what they think and even to object to the demands from adults when they have good reasons. Teaching them to question**

---

[2] Daniel L. Mc. Ivor. "Incest Treatment Strategies" referred to in: "A Silence to be Broken", published by Multnomah Press.

[3] *Only in Los Angeles, California more than 30,000 children are used for child pornography. Source: Earl Wilson. "Let's break the silence". Hope for the victims of incest. Vida Editorial.*

and to suggest; to create in them an open nature without inhibitions. This can be difficult to handle for authoritative parents, but it's the best way to protect them."

As I regarded my wife, I couldn't conceal the wave of anxiety that began to choke me. Drops of sweat ran down my forehead. I took out a handkerchief from my pocket and began to wipe my face.

I gave Alma the book "Internal Freedom" so that she would read it, but if I had known what had happened to her... I might have shook her, I might have yelled directly in her face: *"Alma, it's all right to say NO! It's all right to complain and express your doubts! You have the right to reject the blame of others, you can change your opinion, you can openly say 'I don't know' or 'I don't understand'. Free yourself from complexes of guilt! It's all right to demand that things be explained to you! It's healthy not to be liked by everyone! You'll never be loved by anyone if you don't take the chance that someone will hate you!"*

A lump in my throat made me lower my head. I felt defeated and embraced Lisbeth.

Why don't they teach children assertiveness in school just like they teach math?

Concerned, I moved back a little and asked my wife:

"Physical instincts can be very deceiving. Tell me something: In order to prevent the possibilities of incest, is it better to increase the distance between a father and his daughter?"

Lisbeth answered with immediate certainty:

"Never that. It's exactly **the opposite... Fathers who help with the feedings, the changing of diapers and the growth of their children, in a CLOSE way, <u>from babyhood</u>, have a better and healthier perspective of how vulnerable children are. They learn to love them and to never commit the atrocity of distancing themselves emotionally so much that they wish to get physically close to them, in a 'sexual' way...** On one occasion I heard a man confess that he lived so physically and emotionally DISTANT from his daughter, that he saw her simply as a little woman and it was that which led him to molest her. He had blocked out the idea that she was a little girl and besides that, she was his daughter... **A father that is intrinsically CLOSE, that teaches his children sports, arts, sciences, that prays with them, that talks to them about their emotions, that listens to them, that watches them grow and learns to love them just the way they are, cannot block out his relationship to them...**"

I was relieved listening to her answer. I was worried that parents of today, who are already distant, might have to stay even further away from their little ones to avoid these risks. It was comforting to know that the opposite was required: ***Closeness...***

"And when a child is already immersed in the problem, how can you help?"

"The child who is trapped by an incestous pervert, needs *someone different to trust*, someone who replaces the offender in time and gives legal support to help leave the past behind becoming an understanding mentor... It takes *someone* to tell the child he is NOT GUILTY, that the offender is an unstable person who also needs help, as well as teaching the child to understand, forgive and look ahead; *someone* who doesn't lose control or exaggerate saying the child's life is ruined. The child needs to learn how to play again, to feel accepted and act like a normal person. This mentor shows the child the possibility of identifying with a new and different parental figure."

"It's a whole process..." I said, sadly overwhelmed.

"Maybe there's still time to help Alma," she said. "It will be very hard, Zahid, but I want you to know something." She looked up at me with a decided and sincere expression on her face. "For me, for you, for our past... Because our experience changed us into better people, if you let me and we manage to find her soon, I will become that *someone* she needs."

I wanted to kiss her, thankful for the hope that she was giving me, but I didn't because I was still confused. Suddenly Uncle Ro came to mind. If it hadn't been for that damned pervert...

I took two steps back, ready to leave.

"Where are you going?"

"Don't leave. I'll be back in half an hour."

When I was in front of the old building, I analyzed it carefully before entering. The video rental business was closed and in its place there was a little restaurant.

I looked at the staircase done in old tiles; I had hit myself against the edges when my father had pushed me and I had fallen down them. I went up the stairs breathing in the smells of memories, as if the unpainted walls had in its particles the intense vibrations of all our suffering. I went by the door of what used to be my home, the door that was forced by the attackers who left me without an eye, the door that I once opened to find my dad's drunken orgy with his half-naked friends, the door that had been locked when my uncle molested Alma.

I looked up.

My grandmother had died five years ago and Ro remarried. It seemed strange but now I understood why he had become distant when my parents moved. He didn't attend my wedding and never answered any of the postcards that I sent him.

I arrived, catching my breath. I wasn't sure *I could peacefully confront* Ro, as the norm dictated, when I'd actually set eyes on him again.

I knocked on the door very hard until my knuckles hurt, moved by an uncontained rush of adrenaline.

His wife, who I didn't know, opened the door. I pushed her aside as I went in.

"I'm here to see my father's brother..."

The woman looked at me with surprise and fear.

"Who are you?"

"Ro, you old bastard!" I yelled, ignoring the woman. "Come out of your room!"

He came out wearing slippers and shuffled forward without realizing what was happening.

I looked at him for a few seconds feeling how the rage was taking control of me. It was something beyond my will.

"Why are you barging in like this?" he tried to complain.

I didn't let him finish. I rushed up to him and grabbed him by the collar.

"You sick dirty pig!"

"What's going on?"

I turned slightly to talk to the woman, who was scared, watching us.

"Lady. This man is a miserable degenerate that molested my sister for many years. He started to abuse her when she was a little girl with the excuse of helping our family and he kept on doing it behind our backs for years... He's a treacherous child molester that cannot be trusted."

Ro stuttered, trying to free himself.

"Get out... get out... of here right now."

My confused mind couldn't understand what Lisbeth had explained to me about the abuser being someone who also needed help. I used to help many people, but this guy... I wanted to see him burning in hell.

"You want me to leave this house, you demonic bastard? The apartment house that you used as a hideout sneaking up those old wooden stairs after you molested your niece? How can you have the audacity to live in a place that must remind you every second of your perverse acts? You are a corrupted, vicious, putrid scum bag!"

Ro freed himself and tried to run to his room but I was able to grab him by the robe before he managed to close the door.

I pushed him violently until his back was against the wall and in position to punch him in the face with all my might. He would have lost his false teeth as well as broken a few of his real ones, but just one second before, I stopped. I was gasping for breath. My confused mind couldn't think about the consequences, but after many years of learning how to control myself, my inner conscience stopped me from taking revenge with my own hands. Since I lost my eye, I placed all my need for revenge in God's hands and felt with absolute certainty that my attackers would be dealt with justly and get what they deserved in due time. I could never hurt anyone directly! I didn't owe anyone anything, that's why I had succeeded! I remembered the letter.

"Perhaps you can't help me. I know that you'd give your full sight for me, if it were necessary, but I don't want to be another burden."

She was not wrong... My sight and my life.

I lifted old Ro as best as I could and dragged him to the balcony while he muttered to his wife to get the gun.

I picked him up putting his head over the railing and made him look down, seeing what I had seen when my sister was being attacked on the lower floor.

"Would you like to feel what it's like to fall into space without anyone to help you?"

I pushed him until half of his body was suspended in thin air.

"If you know how to fall, maybe you won't kill yourself. Try..."

"Please," he begged, terrified as he realized that I was serious.

"Let him go!"

The woman stood behind us, aiming the gun directly at me. As I released the tension from holding Ro, he quickly grabbed the railing in order not to fall.

The old woman cried and was trembling like a school girl who unexpectedly has been asked to go up to the front of the class to give a speech. I realized that the gun couldn't be loaded and I could tell by the way she was shaking, that she definitely had no idea of how to use it.

I turned back to my uncle who was on guard, but was heavy and clumsy. I pushed him back. He hit the side of the balcony and fell on his side with his legs open like a broken doll.

If at that moment I had kicked him in the genitals, with all of my fury and due to his position, for sure I could have burst at least one of his testicles, but it was a very low way of taking revenge. I was not the impulsive eighteen year old anymore who had destroyed the hide-out of his opponents.

I examined him on the floor without being able to hold back my tears of controlled rage.

I realized that this man was evil, that a terrible sentence had fallen on him, caused by his own actions.

"You will live in horrible bitterness," I told him, "you will die alone and poisoned; you will never have peace. This is a definite *and fatal Law: 'It's normal to be tempted and stumble, but beware the adult who makes a little child stumble!, the punishment that awaits him is so bad that it would be better for him to wear a large millstone around his neck and be drowned in the depths of the sea.'*[4] I feel pity for you. The worst for you is yet to come."

Without saying another word, I turned around and walked towards the door, waving past the terrified woman who was still shaking, with her arms outstretched, holding the gun that pointed down.

---

[4] *Holy Bible. Lucas 17:1*

17

Flying over quicksand

On my way back I reflected that, in order to succeed, two basic elements are required: preparation and a sense of urgency. This last point needs to become a decisive habit of assertiveness that prevents a person from being passive or shrugging their shoulders when facing certain circumstances. A successful person is, in essence, diligent and enterprising.

I felt a little confused since I had never thought that this sense of urgency could lead to violence. Certainly, Adolf Hitler had preparation and *a sense of urgency*.

"Right," I refuted, "but he didn't have any moral values."

I asked the cab driver to lend me the pencil that he carried behind his ear for a few minutes. I took out one of my business cards and wrote on the back what I would later call: *"The formula to attain human value"*:

HUMAN VALUE=KINDNESS+KNOWLEDGE+ACTIONS

KINDNESS + KNOWLEDGE (Without actions) = Illusions of frustrated, intelligent men.
KINDNESS + ACTIONS (Without knowledge) = Ignorance of well intentioned people.
ACTIONS + KNOWLEDGE (Without kindness) = Atrocities of evil leaders.

I contemplated my new theory, calibrating how simple it was and the way it proposed an authentic model to measure the real value of people.

I gave the pencil back to the driver, thanking him.

I refused to accept that the righteous anger I felt for Ro made my actions the same as the atrocity of an "evil leader". I **didn't l**ack the third element of the formula. Basically, I was a good person, only hurt by the way that Alma had been sexually abused by him, in fact, I felt badly for having attacked him, but not sorry I did it.

I found Lisbeth standing in the same place where I had left her, leaning against the railing, looking down, thoughtfully.

"Anything new?" I asked.

"No. Where did you go?"

"To get rid of the pressure that was killing me."

I then knocked again at the door of the apartment, prepared to demolish it. We couldn't just stand there anymore.

Once more, the woman from the opposite apartment came out.

"I'm sorry," I said. "Can't you tell us *anything* about the person that lives here?"

The neighbor realized that we wouldn't go away until we found an answer.

"The only thing I know," she announced with a scanty voice, "is that she has a friend on the sixth floor; apartment eighteen."

Still baffled by the unexpected information, I began to thank her, but she closed the door again without waiting for a response.

We left a note for my parents and went up the stairs immediately until we arrived at the right apartment.

For a moment, neither one of us dared to knock at the door.

Since we had begun our trip, we had received one blow after another until the pain in my broken heart wasn't sure it could take much more.

Before knocking, the door opened and a well-dressed young woman came out.

The scare was mutual.

"Can I help you?"

"Yes... no... I mean... is this apartment eighteen?"

She studied us skeptically. On her door were two large numbers: a one and an eight. Lisbeth jumped in to rescue the situation.

"Please excuse our intrusion, but we've been looking for several hours for a young woman named Alma Duarte. We're her family. She wrote imploring us to come but it's been very difficult to find her. Can you tell us anything?"

"How do I know that you're not the police?"

We remained still. Could it be that my sister had some problem with the law? The severity of Alma's situation began to penetrate into the complexities of my discernment. Perhaps they were looking for her for possession or trafficking of drugs... in addition to the fact that... her *trade* was full of dangers.

My movements were clumsy as I took the letter out of my pocket and handed it to the woman. She analyzed it carefully.

"It's her writing," she muttered. "Wait a minute."

She went inside the apartment and closed the door.

"I think this is it" Lisbeth said to me, "I have the feeling that this time we're very close to finding your sister."

I nodded.

After a while, the young woman returned, examining us; her face expressed cautious hope.

"Please, come in."

We walked behind her.

The place was dark although clean and well laid out. A central window at the back of the living room might have provided enough light, but the curtains were almost closed. The sun beams only came through the center, marking a triangular path with the vertex at the glass and the base towards us.

I felt extremely restless. I could sense that Alma was there.

"Would you like to sit down?"

"No. I mean... Thanks. Later."

Suddenly, a human shape moved from the shadows by the curtain into the opening where the light came streaming in.

It was a thin body that blocked the sun rays. A silhouette against the light that seemed to have an aura, due to the golden beams surrounding it.

"Alma?"

She didn't answer.

She was standing with her shoulders slightly bent and nervously moving her fingers.

I advanced impatiently towards her.

At each step, the vision became clearer until she was in front of me. Focusing on her face, I froze shocked by the horrifying changes that I found facing me.

She was my sister, but *she was not..*

She was alive, but *she was not.*

Her aged appearance frightened me. I tried to hide my astonishment and managed a fake smile.

"Zahid..." she muttered.

"You've changed..." I said to her.

"You can't even imagine *how much*."

I began to lift my hands to embrace her, but she stopped me by putting hers on my forearms.

Her hair was dyed, burnt by the excessive use of chemicals. Her face was very pale with deep wrinkles between her eyes and large circles under them. She had pajamas on, although it was obvious she had combed her hair and put on some make up in a hurry.

"As... soon as I received your... letter," I explained, nervously hesitating, "we came here to look for you but you didn't put a return address, so the hospital told us..."

She slouched over, defeated.

"So, you already know."

I raised my hand again to put it lovingly on her shoulder. My mind couldn't comprehend seeing her like this.

"We've all suffered, Alma. We've faced serious problems, but we've recovered. Why didn't...?"

I interrupted myself. I didn't know how to get through to her, what to say to her. I didn't want to make the mistake of making her feel attacked or cornered.

"Why *what*?" she answered defensively and evaded the physical contact by stepping back.

Lisbeth was in the center of the room. Both women were face to face.

"This is my wife," I said, following her, "we got married four months ago. I really wanted you to come to the wedding, but no one knew where you were."

She smiled sadly and slowly shuffled to the couch and let herself collapse on it.

Her friend approached us and excused herself explaining she had to leave.

"Make yourselves at home. Alma, I'll see you later."

My sister waved good-bye and sighed.

"Well, well..." she said. "Zahid, the successful one... after, how many years?"

Her question was at the same time nostalgic and accusing.

I came closer and crouched down in front of her.

"Sis, we've come for you. You must get out of here, we want to help you."

She glared at me strangely and I was so close to her I noticed her eyes were opaque. She was looking at me yet without really seeing me.

"Are you feeling all right?"

She leaned back and closed her eyes.

"I didn't sleep well."

Then I detected something abnormal about her voice.

I sat down next to her but didn't try to touch her again.

"Lisbeth is the director of one of the best centers that help women," I said to her. "If you come with us, I assure you that things will change."

"No one wants things to change," she muttered, without opening her eyes.

"That's not what you said in your letter."

"I never should have written it."

"Don't say that. Just let us help you." I put my hand on hers and she reacted again. I misjudged her. I believed she was weak and that her mind was distracted. She pushed me forcibly and stood before me, with an attitude of true defiance.

"You really *grew up*, Zahid, because you always had more strength, more courage, more determination. I, on the other hand, simply *aged.* I didn't have emotional support, I lived in a destroyed home with an embittered mother, a sick father and an uncle..." she smiled sarcastically... "a very special one... I'm disappointed with men, sick of love, sick of so much filth."

She stood up furiously and started pacing around the room. Lisbeth approached her, trying to calm her down.

"I understand you, Alma. Really I do. If you let us help you I promise you that..."

"No..." she confronted my wife. "Everyone who has ever promised me anything, in the end have only *used* me, lied and toyed with me. Besides, what gives you the right to come and teach me anything? Who do you think you're talking to?"

"If you don't begin to trust again," interrupted my wife, raising her voice, "you'll drown alone..."

"Trust? There isn't an honest person alive! Everyone hides behind their own selfish personal interests. I'm not so easy to fool. Go away. No one needs you anyway..."

After listening to her bitter judgement for a moment, we doubted our mission.

"Alma," I said, moving towards her, with a sorrow that was turning into despair, "you can't trust *me* either...?"

Maybe she remembered the desperate sincerity of her letter written in a moment in which "she still thought with some lucidity"; perhaps our childhood fear was reawakened as she remembered how we faced the damages of what our parents had done to us; maybe she recalled our secret alliance in that hospital room in which she cared for me and in which I was enraged because of the injustice that I couldn't assimilate; maybe she simply recognized me, because she lowered her guard.

"In you, Zahid, yes, I'd like to trust... but..." she interrupted herself, "everyone has only wanted my body..." she stuttered. "Since I was a little girl it's been like that. When the most terrible and unexplainable things happened around me, Ro embraced me and caressed me with tenderness. I was small... I didn't know what he was doing, but I was so afraid and needed love so badly..." She paused to take a deep breath and continued: "When I started high school I realized the depraved enormity of what he had done to me; I began to date a boy and when he touched me, I wasn't able to say no. In fact, I was quite shy but in that aspect I knew many things... I let him... I accepted whatever my classmate wanted... As time went by, many men sought me out... I learned to handle them with strategies that no girl of my age knew. I was aggressive. I hurt many of them. I became embittered to the core of my being. An older man became aware of my degradation. He promised to help me if I went away with him. He exploited me. He tricked me. When he was satiated, he threw me out in the street. I felt like a piece of rotten flesh who had lost the right to go back to her parents or to go and look for you, Zahid... You were 'the example to follow'. How could I explain to you my downfall? Besides, I had no strength to move... I knew that wherever I went someone would want to use me. In the streets I found other paths."

I wanted to answer, but I only managed to articulate a couple of guttural sounds and remained silent.

"Thanks for coming, but it's useless," she said. "Two siblings of the same family can have different talents and fates. I was the twisted one, you the perfect... Let's leave it at that."

The problem wasn't asking her if she wished to be helped or not. She was convinced of her ominous fate, she firmly believed in an involuntary destiny that had poisoned her and was useless to fight. The challenge consisted in making her see that she had the necessary elements to change, that she was at this point in her life because she had allowed it; that her deviation, for which she felt a certain pride, was in reality an option that she had chosen.

"Since I went to college," I recalled, "I sent you books every month. I wrote to you about the need to fill yourself with positive and new ideas. Did you read any of the material?"

"I'm not much of a reader."

"Does that mean that you didn't read *anything*?"

"I started to, but I stopped."

"On three occasions I took you to an Alanon group. You went with me and promised that you would continue to attend. Did you do it?"

"Zahid, what are you trying to prove? I had many problems, I couldn't comply with rigid systems..."

"That's a lie. After the confrontation I talked to you many times. You would ask me sarcastically if I was going to give you another sermon. You were cynical. Don't blame anyone. You're here because you chose to be."

Alma was ready to fight. She wasn't prepared to feel responsible. She would defend her position of being "a victim of fate".

"Terrible things happened to me," she accused. "I wanted to leave, but people kept pushing me down every step of the way. Besides, I lack your talent and your character. We're not all born with the same capabilities. The masterpieces are created by talented geniuses. The rest of us, the ordinary people, have to be content with moving the garbage from one side to the other."

"That's enough! Don't say that again! You have the talent and the capacity that you want to have! Ordinary people are like that **because they give up**. They're too lazy to pay the price. They want to arrive at the top in a year. They look at those who succeed and minimize them. They say: 'if that poor devil made it, I can easily do it too', but they don't realize the fact that he's worked day and night, that he's dedicated himself and his life to his dreams. Those who are lazy, arrogant and proud end up doing a mediocre job and then feel frustrated when they don't get what they thought would be so easy. They're too lazy to invest time in sowing seeds for the future, Alma. That's it. It's easier to give up than to flap their stiff wings and fly. We would all be able to accomplish similar works to those of Da Vinci, Michael Angelo or Einstein, *if we were prepared to pay the price that they paid.* You didn't want to pay the price. It's simply that. You were apathetic. You had the tools at your disposal, but you didn't even make the smallest attempt to use them and fight... Ideas make you free or a slave. You need to hold onto positive ideas to get out of the quicksand as if they were branches of a tree that are leaning towards you to save you."

A confused disbelief tinged with fear spread across Alma's face. Her brother, far from feeling sorry for her, was pointing out her mistakes without any pity?

"Zahid, you're unfair. You had cancer of the soul and found the exact medicine to cure yourself but you didn't share it with your sister who was also sick. You only said to her: 'Read books and if you're lucky you'll find the secret formula'."

"I'm sorry, Alma," I answered immediately, "for our illness there's no magic formula. The medicine is **to change our attitudes, to achieve a new mentality and increase the energy from our self-esteem;** that is a process based on tremendous PERSONAL effort. If you didn't make the effort, that's your problem. You had the medicine, but you didn't take it because it implied work... You saw a lifeguard in front of you but you didn't want to swim to him."

"But Ro took advantage of my innocence. I didn't know what he was doing to me. I believed that it was normal. When I found out the damage that he had done to me, I felt miserable and worthless."

"That's the second time you've repeated that absurdity. Understand this: no one damaged you, unless you want to think that they did." Lisbeth's words came to mind and I decided to give them a try: ***What ruins life is not an event but the interpretation that you give to it.*** *It's a matter of ideas. Don't limit your way of thinking. What can be normal for one culture, can be wrong for another. If you say 'it's the end,' it is. If, on the contrary, you tell yourself: ''The real ME is still intact, I refuse to swallow this poison and become bitter,' then there's no reason for you to sink...* I'm not trying to make you feel guilty, I only want you to react. I've never said nor will say that I lost an eye to defend you, but, since you mentioned it in your letter, you were not wrong when you assumed that I'd give not only my complete sight but my *whole life* to save yours, but with one condition: that you really wanted to save yourself... Without that wish, without that firm and total decision, dear sister, don't count on me. Go on rotting away if that's what you want..."

Alma remained still. Speechless...

In the room, one could perceive the vibrations of a strong conflict.

There was love, but also resentment... There were reasons, but also outrage. There was darkness, but also rays of light shimmering through the fog of uncertainty and struggle.

Lisbeth approached my sister and put her arm around her.

To my surprise, this time Alma did not object. She began to sob. The spontaneous contact of a sincere friend made her finally feel the weight of her mistakes.

My wife led her to the couch and began to speak to her in a calm, loving way.

"Only with the help of God, was I able to pull myself out of where I had been, the same as your father and Zahid... You know this first-hand."

Alma nodded slightly.

"It doesn't matter where you go," continued Lisbeth, "**It doesn't matter what you have, since what really matters is WHO is at your side. And if God is at your side, there's no crisis that can destroy you... Suffering produces growth, and the victory is for His glory...** You'll overcome your crisis and develop courage. Learn that you shouldn't deposit all of your love and all of your trust in human beings. People are weak and let us down. Understand this, only when you totally give your life, your belongings, your suffering and your love to the Lord, will you find a mission that will give meaning to your existence..."

"It's too late. My life can't have any meaning... even if I wanted it to."

"Of course it can! It's a matter of decision, of abandonment, of surrender. I gave a son to God. Do you know what that means? He took him in His hands and offered me the peace of knowing that He would look after him. In the same way, put your life exactly as it is, even with all your damaged feelings, before the Lord and tell Him: 'It is yours'. Let Him fill your empty soul, your afflicted spirit, let Him clean your mind, let Him fill your heart with His love. The rotten tree where you sheltered yourself was swallowed by quicksand, you fell into the mire and you've stayed there for years. Shake off the foul mud, have the courage, the strength and the faith to move your stiff wings, until you've managed to rise up and fly off towards the fertile forest that's waiting for you..."

Alma looked up at us. In her eyes there was no more anger, only a great regret mixed with gratefulness.

"I've damaged my body..." she articulated. "Your words comfort me a lot, I'm prepared to attempt it. I swear to you... but... Zahid, tell me something, what did they tell you at the hospital?"

"About the heroin and the prostitution."

She looked as if she were waiting for me to say more. Seeing that I didn't continue, the sinister gloom of a dark secret shadowed her gaze. She bowed her head, filled with a profound anguish.

"I'm glad that they didn't tell you the *whole* story... because... I... needed to hear what you've said to me and... perhaps you might have hesitated..."

"The *whole* story? What do you mean, Alma?"

"There is something that you don't know."

"My God..."

"A few months ago I went into shock because of an overdose."

"We know that."

"When they took me to St. John's Hospital, they ran all sorts of tests..."

A chill of terror traveled through my body. I recalled what the psychologist had said: "W*e tried to help her but things became complicated. After the diagnosis she fell into a deep depression"*.

After the diagnosis?

I closed my eyes hoping it wouldn't be the logical consequence of her lifestyle. Unfortunately, it was truc.

Bluntly, she said to me:

"I have AIDS..."

Epilogue

We had to deal with the problem one step at a time.

The first part was the detoxification process. To complete this, my sister had to be readmitted into St. John's Hospital.

To witness the withdrawal symptoms of a heroin addict is not a pleasant experience for anyone. Alma suffered acute diarrhea, vomiting, fevers, hallucinations, lack of appetite and sleep. More than once, she had to be tied down because of the anxiety attacks where she lost all ability to reason and became aggressively violent.

As she had offered, my wife supported her physically, morally and spiritually. My parents also helped and they kept a close eye on the process.

I have to confess that my life has not been the same since we found her.

I've finally understood, but not without grief, that to rise through the skyscraper, to obtain degrees, wealth and prestige, loses its value if we can't share it with those we love the most.

Lisbeth did all that was humanly possible to help her, however, I felt hurt watching my wife's frustration. I thought that maybe it reminded her of Martin, the father of her son who was also a drug addict; fortunately, when he got out of jail, she never heard of him again...

We've all gone through some very hard times and this has transformed all of us in distinctive ways.

Who would have thought that only a few days before the opening of my new business headquarters, I'd find myself involved in such an enormous emotional upheaval!

I couldn't disappoint the enthusiastic expectations of my colleagues, so even though my state of mind was not at its best, I attended the inauguration ceremony.

It was a spontaneous speech since I went unprepared. I don't remember what I said. To tell you the truth, while I was speaking, I wasn't thinking about my employees but about Alma... Indirectly, I was telling her that the mind can always climb out of any problem, that the spirit is capable of overcoming any sickness forcing it out of the body, that it didn't matter how long she had to live, she had to get up and give it the best she's got.

At my company, they never knew what the real motivation for my speech was, but people liked it, to the point that someone, as I spoke, managed to write down a fragment of it. They framed it and hung it in the entry hall of the main offices.

THE SECOND CHANCE

There is a saying that says: "If it doesn't hurt, It doesn't do any good."

The only people who can win important competitions are the athletes, students, professionals, heads of families and businessmen that understand this.

In the struggle, all the contenders begin to suffer when they reach the border of fatigue. It's a clear frontier in which many abandon the race, convinced that they have reached their limit.

However, those who don't give up when they reach the point of pain, those who make a conscious effort to accept the suffering that others avoid, suddenly break the barrier and enter a new stage that is called a ***SECOND CHANCE.***

This SECOND CHANCE is similar to a SECOND WIND when racing, exactly when a much greater energy returns, the lungs breathe better, the cardiovascular system works more efficiently and the brain sharpens its senses.

One can only win when the SECOND WIND gives the person a ***SECOND CHANCE****.*

Only in this stage can great inventions be created.

Only here can the masterpieces be accomplished, as well as the enterprises that make history.

This company is derived from the ***SECOND CHANCE****.*

Those who work at it know how to insist and to resist.

We know that by giving more than what we have to give, we will receive more than what we expect to receive.

We know that our results are superior because they happen after the fatigue, because they weren't easy or free, because we have the position that we have after having made an extra effort in our field.

Our love for doing things with excellence is what keeps us together.

Our devotion to achieve and preserve a leadership that is priceless.

Our complicity for having arrived together at the point of suffering and having overcome it to stay united in the ***SECOND CHANCE****, where we don't suffer anymore, where everything is results...*

Our conviction is that by ***APPLYING THIS MESSAGE AND SPREADING IT,*** *we are associated in one of the largest and most important projects in history.*

It meant a huge sacrifice for my sister to stop doing drugs.

She fought against the terrible monster for more than six months. To watch her struggle and suffer was like witnessing the demons who possessed her, revealing themselves before they were finally destroyed.

I cared for her night and day.

One morning, she said to me that she really wanted to recover and that she wanted to live through the rest of her life in a dignified way, but she didn't know how.

"I have the AIDS virus in my body," she said to me, "but it hasn't manifested itself yet. Zahid, help me. I know that Lisbeth also overcame severe traumas. I know that she had the willpower that I lacked. Your own case is interesting too. I need you to explain to me in detail how you found the branches to pull yourself out of the quicksand so you could escape and save yourself. Or better yet," she corrected herself, "you should write a book. That way I can review it, study it, memorize it..."

"I'm not a writer."

"But everything is in your mind," she said to me, smiling, "if you don't want to be, you won't..."

"But I wouldn't want others to be able to read about our private lives."

"On the contrary! Do you know how much it can help others? What good does it do to keep it a secret? There are many people who, like me, don't have the courage to grab hold to a lifesaving branch in order to get out of the quicksand... I now understand that it's my mission to recover as much as possible, but you have to write the book... Please. Look at me straight in the eyes and promise you will..."

My emotional confusion made it very difficult to write these pages, but I did it to fulfill a promise...

Alma left the hospital forty-four pounds under her normal weight.

The day that she was released from the hospital we prayed together.

She forgave Ro and prayed to God for him, although we never saw him again.

I was deeply moved listening to her prayer.

My father had a party to welcome her, although with only a few close friends.

Alma did what she should have done fifteen years earlier: She began to read, to go to conferences and attend support groups... I know for a fact that she read this book at least five times, highlighted it and made some charts summarizing what, in her opinion, was the most important.

She was asked to pay a very high price for doing drugs. Accepting her reckoning, she stopped blaming others, worked very hard and gave a hundred percent of all she had inside of her in order to succeed. She finally found in her life a second chance.

Up until now, as I write this epilogue, my sister is alive, but spiritually she died to her flesh and was born again in spirit. Currently she travels all over the world actively participating in a group that organizes events for AIDS prevention.

She confirmed a truth to me that before I couldn't fully comprehend with all of its overwhelming force: It's never too late.

It doesn't matter what we might have lived, it doesn't matter what mistakes we might have made, it doesn't matter what opportunities we might have allowed to pass by; age doesn't matter, we are always on time to say "enough", to listen to the voice inside of us that calls for perfection, to shake off the mire and fly very high, far away from the quicksand...

This book was printed on by Imprentor, S.A. de C.V.
ESD-5-54-01-M-01-02